# The Secret of Collecting
# Girls' Series Books

## Featuring Nancy Drew®, Judy Bolton, Kay Tracey,
## Beverly Gray, Penny Parker and Ruth Fielding

## by John Axe

**Hobby House Press, Inc.**
Grantsville, MD 21536
**www.hobbyhouse.com**

# Dedication

To thank my sisters
Bette Ann, Patty and Susan
for all they have done for me.

# Acknowledgments

I am grateful to all those who have helped me with this project.

I thank everyone at Hobby House Press, Inc. for their input and their professionalism, especially Gary R. Ruddell, Carolyn Cook, Brian Haefs, Virginia Ann Heyerdahl and Brenda Wiseman.

I appreciate the aid and influence of my fellow collectors and researchers. I could not have managed without Janet Anderson Abrahams, Roger Abrahams, Marilyn Danielson of Danielson Antiques, Kate Emburg of *The Whispered Watchword*, Donna Felger, Barbara Gilland, Sue Grossman, Sue Grotyohann, Kenneth Hopping, Shirley Karaba, D.J. Layhe, Garrett Lothe of *Susabella Passengers and Friends*, Peggy McKissick of Twice-Loved Books, Gil O'Gara of *Yellowback Library* and Lorraine Rogers. I must also acknowledge David Edwards for his Series Book Catalog and Donna Mehalco, Branch Manager of ComDoc.

I will always appreciate Marjorie Eckstein who answered my letter in 1994. And most of all I will remember her mother, Margaret Sutton, who answered my letter in 1952 and from whom I received my first encouragement ever.

Additional copies of this book may be purchased at $19.95 (plus postage and handling) from
**Hobby House Press, Inc.**
1 Corporate Drive, Grantsville, MD 21536
1-800-554-1447
**www.hobbyhouse.com**
or from your favorite bookstore or dealer.
© 2000 John Axe

Printed in the United States of America.

ISBN: 0-87588-577-2

# Table of Contents

# Foreword

Fifty years ago this past summer I began collecting series books in earnest. I already had many of them, as I had received some Bobbsey Twins books and others as Christmas presents, but in the summer of 1949 I began buying my own books. We lived on a farm in Pennsylvania and back then it was more difficult for me to get to a store where children's books were sold than it would be to get to Paris today. But in those days we had another way to shop: Montgomery Ward's catalog.

The first book I ordered was *Heidi's Children*. I think that it cost 65 cents and 10 cents for postage. I still have this book, as well as every other book I ever had as a child and they all have their dust jackets and are in very good condition. The cover of *Heidi's Children* states that it was written by Charles Tritten, Johanna Spyri's translator. The illustrations, including the dust jacket, are by Pelagie Doane. Now I know that *Heidi's Children* was actually written by Margaret Sutton, the author of the Judy Bolton books, of which the first eighteen were illustrated by Pelagie Doane. It is because of Margaret Sutton and Pelagie Doane that I have maintained my interest in series books all these years.

Like many collectors of their childhood memorabilia, I did not concentrate much on my series books for a long time but for several years now I have come back to them with the same passion I had fifty years ago, although in the meantime I bought series books at flea markets, books sales and other places, if they were a bargain, and put them away. I now wish I had done more of that. The books I liked as a child were Judy Bolton, Nancy Drew, the Hardy Boys, the Five Little Peppers, the Albert Payson Terhune series of dog stories and the Louisa May Alcott books. I also have many volumes of other series, but I never tried to complete the sets, or else I was not able to.

The money for my books came from my allowance, birthday gifts and what I earned. When I was about eight years old I got a job during the school year washing blackboards for Miss Adams who gave me a quarter a week for this. Soon Mrs. Moore had me do her boards also and right after that Mrs. Fruit, in the room next to her, did the same. What I earned from these high school teachers came out to a book a week, as most series books cost 75 cents each then. By 1951, the Grosset & Dunlap books were 85 cents and before long they were 95 cents each, but by that time I had a paper route, which paid more than blackboard washing did.

Sometime in 1949, while we were playing in the basement of my cousin's house, I came across *The Mystery of the Ivory Charm*, an old thick Nancy Drew book with orange endpapers. I was told that I could have it when I wanted to borrow it. To me, Nancy Drew was "adult" reading matter and very exciting because of the cliff hangers at the end of each chapter. That Christmas my "Want List" included Nancy

Drew books, and I got *The Clue of the Leaning Chimney* and *The Mystery of the Tolling Bell*. This resulted in an addiction that did not end until I had the entire set of Nancy Drew books.

In Sunday School, I told my friend Donna about Nancy Drew. She insisted that there was a better series to read and loaned me the first Judy Bolton book, *The Vanishing Shadow*. This mystery was so advanced for me at that age that I did not fully understand all the plot nuances, but again I became addicted and acquired the whole set of Judy Bolton books. For Christmas of 1951 alone I received four of this set from three different people.

Although I spent all the money I could get on books, each one of them was very important to me. I purchased dozens of series books (and others) in the early 1950s. I can remember where I acquired most of them and even where they were located on the shelf in the store. By that time, I had found several stores that carried series books. Back then small department stores and stationery shops had a small selection of series books that they stocked for Christmas. I was their best customer on a yearly basis. My favorite place to buy books was a toy shop of a kind that no longer exists. This store carried a better line of toys than such places as G.C. Murphy and Woolworth's. During the Christmas season, its front window was full of the latest Madame Alexander dolls, which was about the only place in the store where there was much of a display. This was the old-fashioned sort of long, narrow store with an unpainted wooden floor and most things were kept in boxes up on shelves or in drawers. The back half of the store was for wallpaper and paint, probably the merchandise that made the store profitable. In between these two sections was a large square bookcase with series books on all four sides. They were arranged in shelves from near the floor to above my eye level. At that time merchandise was presented to the customer after it was paid for differently than it is today. A book was wrapped in heavy brown paper and carefully tied up with string instead of being casually dropped into a bag.

The book I bought there was *The Password to Larkspur Lane*, the first Nancy Drew I purchased. This was in January 1950. I pulled out each of the Nancy Drew books and studied them and picked this one because of the picture on the dust jacket. The dramatic scene on the cover of the book shows Nancy kneeling at a high wire fence; an old lady in a wheelchair is on the other side. A mean-looking man is coming toward them from a mansion in the background and the old lady is cautioning Nancy to remain silent. This is the sort of picture that tells that something exciting and dangerous is about to happen. I eventually had the whole set of Nancy Drew books, but each one that I bought was because the picture on the cover made me want it, based on

## National League of American Penwomen
### INCORPORATED
### LONG ISLAND BRANCH

5 Brookwold Court, Baldwin, N. Y.
February 18th, 1952

Dear Johnnie:

I was most interested in your
letter of January 29th telling me about your
home town, Mercer, Pennsylvania. You guessed
right. I do come from Pennsylvania, but not
from Mercer. I suppose there are lots of
towns similar to the Farringdon of my story.
Actually, it is not a real place, and neither
is Roulsville (although there is a town named
Roulette) and a real Dry Brook Hollow. The
town I used as a model for Farringdon is my
home town, Coudersport, Pa. You can see that
I couldn't call it by its real name without
making my stories too factual. I've combined
fact and fiction in all of them except JEMIMA
which is a true story. There will be another
historical story some day. I have it partly
written. It's the story of VIRGINIA REED OF
THE DONNER PARTY. However, another Judy is
due and right now I am busy on that.

Enclosed you will find my
picture which I have autographed for you.
Just paste it inside your book and you will
have an autographed book. Just one final
tip if you want to be an author. Have a
strong plot, but create your own characters
and write as you feel.

Good luck, and best wishes,

Margaret Sutton

Letter from Margaret Sutton to John Axe, February 18, 1952.

what I had come to expect from the mystery stories in the series.

This is not a unique situation. I have friends who also bought their books after carefully examining all the pictures on the covers of the ones available at the time. Janet went for *The Clue in the Old Album*, which she considers has the most beautiful Nancy Drew dust jacket picture. She can also remember where the book was on the shelf in the store and, like me, can remember what shop each one came from although there are many. I am lucky that I still have all my books, as well as the memories associated with them. I can remember where I was when I read a certain book, what the weather was like that day and what was going on at home during the time I was reading it. Naturally I kept a list of the books I read and I gave each one a rating. All these details that we remember show the importance of series books in our lives.

I had another friend who later became a major league baseball player and a rookie of the year. Needless to mention, he did not think much of Nancy Drew and Judy Bolton and introduced me to the Hardy Boys. I did not find this series as "adult" as Judy Bolton but the adventures of Frank and Joe were more thrilling than any I had read. The Hardys were one of the few boys series books available for sale to me and the only series the library had so I went through them, and in the meantime sampled Kay Tracey, Penny Parker, Cherry Ames and Beverly Gray, none of which left an impression on me. I acquired each new Judy Bolton book until 1956 because of my special relationship with Margaret Sutton, although they did not seem as good as they once did.

As a series, I always liked the Judy Bolton books the best. The characters in the Nancy Drew books were mainly girls; the Hardy Boys and a couple of their chums dominated those books. The Judy Bolton books placed strong emphasis on both boy and girl auxiliary characters and, unlike both the Nancy Drew and Hardy Boys books, there are important characters who are quite a bit younger or quite a bit older than the main protagonists. I did not analyze it quite this way when I was young, but this is the element that must have appealed to me, as it seemed like the real situations I knew, although the last several books in the series have plots that are not as realistic or believable as they were in the first twenty-three or so books.

On January 29, 1952, I wrote to Margaret Sutton, using as my excuse a query as to whether Judy's hometown in Pennsylvania was my own hometown there. (It was not.) Mrs. Sutton wrote back on February 18, 1952, and also included her photograph, which I had requested. It took me forty-two years to write back and thank her for the picture and, in June of 1998, I had the good fortune to meet her for the first time in Coudersport, Pennsylvania, the setting of the Judy Bolton Mysteries. I will always be glad that I attended Potter County's "Margaret Sutton Days" because it will probably be the last time that Margaret Sutton (age ninety-five then) will dominate a public event.

My series books in 1953. On the top shelf are Judy Bolton books; on the middle shelf are Nancy Drew books.

Another view of my bookcase in 1953. In the top shelf, center, are Kay Tracey books; on the center shelf, right, are Penny Parker books.

People who do not do so wonder why we who collect books do. I am always amazed when somebody comes into my house, sees all the books and (always) asks, "Have you read all those books?" I remember a summer day when I was about three years old. I was lying on the grass with a Bible that I had asked for after I saw them in Sunday School. I studied the printed page and thought that I could read it; of course I couldn't. I finally did learn to read before I went to first grade in a one-room country school. One afternoon, when I was in first grade, the teacher began reading *Beautiful Joe* to the students because everyone was upset after Frances Thompson's mother came to the school to let us know that Frances died the night before. The beginning of this book is certainly far from uplifting, but I really liked Frances and it did distract me. And I learned a lot of new things by listening to the teacher reading *Beautiful Joe* and by reading many more books myself, up to the point where I taught History in a university, based a great deal on things that I had read.

After all this time, I still re-read my series books over and over. When I read them and when I look at the pictures on those dust jackets I am young again, my little sister is still alive, and I cannot wait for Christmas because I may get some more books on my "Want List."

# CHAPTER 1

# Introduction

## Values

I admit that value guides for any collectible item are not necessarily a good thing. However, they are a useful thing. If something is worth collecting it is worth conserving and hence it has a value.

Price guides usually carry the disclaimer "The prices are guides; they are not absolutes" or something similar. It is the purpose of this book to show many of the most popular girls' series books that are collected in large numbers and to establish retail prices for them. The author recognizes the fact that when prices are established for any collectible with a book it can cause those who do not understand the product or its value to place a price on it that has little bearing with reality. In other words, it can cause prices to rise. But on the other hand, if this is the case, it can also cause the value of something already owned in a collection to escalate in worth.

The price ranges given for series books in this volume have a very wide difference between the lowest price and the highest price. This is because **condition is everything in pricing a used book**. Rarity is also an important factor, so this is reflected in the price. In general, **a series book without a dust jacket is worth only a fraction of the same one with a dust jacket**. And the better the condition of the dust jacket, the more the book is worth. Example:

**Beverly Gray, Sophomore; Format IV** (1950s) **$3.00 - $25.00.**

This means that a book in poor condition without a dust jacket is valued at $3.00; one in fine condition with an excellent dust jacket is valued at $25.00. That is to say, the range is from the worst book of the format to the best example. Books that are in horrible condition are not considered, as they have no value. "First Editions" are taken into consideration by the fact that they are "Format I."

Nothing is going to prevent a person who does not understand old books, let alone series books, from listing them for sale as this: "Wonderful old example of Heidi book, probably first edition, a must for any Heidi collector. Cover loose and torn, ink marks, the first few pages missing, but very good for its age. Only $19.95." The book is actually about five years old and has no value for a collector and should

be priced at under a dollar. But don't bother to inform the seller of this, because he doesn't want to know it. He is not seeking knowledge or information; he is seeking a sale. Information would only offend him. Make your statement by ignoring the book.

The prices given in this book are those that are currently asked for books by knowledgeable book dealers and collectors. The Internet and eBay are taken into consideration. Anyone can ask any price they choose to; anyone can pay any price they want to.

In the past, collectors of old books who were seeking to add to their collections depended on book dealers; dealers' "lists"; advertisements in magazines, newsletters and journals; antiquarian book shows; antique shops; flea markets; auctions; and other sources. This is the slow way to add to a collection. Now a collection can be completed more quickly with Internet listings and auctions on the Internet. How long would it take a person searching for Nancy Drew books or Judy Bolton books to locate and look at 1215 books using the older, more traditional methods? On one night, 16 January 2000, to be exact, there were 1130 Nancy Drew books and 85 Judy Bolton books up for auction on eBay. There were also many more copies available through computer listings of books for sale. Computers and the Internet are not for everybody, but this method of collecting is here to stay and it is much more efficient, although nothing will ever replace the search at a book sale or the excitement of seeing one a collector "needs" and can pick up and hold in a shop.

It is true that many prices on eBay auctions are high because two or three people are desperate to have a certain book that day and the next time the same title is up for auction the price may be lower. Or it may be even higher because collectors have seen how much people are willing to pay for it. But bargains can be found even on eBay and not every auction ends up with a "sniper" grabbing it in the last thirty seconds for 50 cents more than you have been bidding for a week.

I have gathered my prices from the all the above sources and from my own evaluation and judgment, having collected series books most of my life.

## Grading the Condition of Books

Most old books and collectible books are sold through "lists" and through mail order. Because of this, accurate wording and descriptions must be used if both the seller and the buyer are to understand the condition of the book. The following guide

for grading books is taken from *AB Bookman's Weekly*, which has been using this reference since 1949. It should be used as the standard for all buyers and sellers of old books.

| | |
|---|---|
| **As New** | The book looks perfect, as it did when first published. |
| **Fine** | The book is close to "as new," but is not totally crisp. |
| **Very Good** | Some signs of wear are present, such as a crease or a tiny tear (called a chip) in the dust jacket. Defects must be noted. |
| **Good** | The book and dust jacket show minor wear but defects are not too distracting. All imperfections must be noted. |
| **Fair** | This is a worn book and/or dust jacket that is complete and acceptable if described properly, with all defects noted. |
| **Poor** | This is a badly worn book, called a "reading copy." It is not worth anything as a collectible. |

The abbreviations for the above are: **AN, FN, VG, GD, FR, PR**.

Two other conditions must be noted in old books: **Ex-libris** means that the book was a library book and has evidence of this with stamped information or card pockets. **Book Club Editions**, no matter what their condition, should always be noted. These two designations are usually scorned by collectors unless the book is very rare and difficult to locate in better condition or in a standard printing.

The lack of a dust jacket must also be noted. It is standard procedure to rate both the dust jacket and the book, with the dust jacket rating listed first. An example of a description would be: "GD/GD. Minor chipping to DJ [dust jacket] spine top and bottom; slightly cocked spine; minor foxing on page ends."

# Cleaning Collectible Books

Some museum curators consider the dirt that is in many artifacts to be part of their originality and do not remove it. An example is the dust and dirt found in Navaho and other Native American rugs and blankets. Other curators realize that dirt causes deterioration and also attracts microscopic pests that, in time, destroy things made of paper, such as books.

I always clean the books I buy because it probably does prolong their lives and it certainly makes them look much better. It can also improve their smell. The following is how I clean my books, based on years of experience in doing this.

First, remove the dust jacket and clean the book itself. Spray some commercial glass cleaner on a paper towel and carefully wipe off the covers of the book. Be careful with this, as the coloring agent in some cloth covers will run or rub off. Never spray a cleaner directly onto the book. Next, clean all the page edges, especially the top edges. Do this carefully with a soft, kneaded eraser, never with a pencil eraser or other hard eraser. Hold the pages tightly together when running the kneaded eraser over them to prevent bending or tearing.

The next process is to microwave the book. This will kill the fungus that causes mildew, which leaves spots, marks and an odor. Fan the pages of the book out and set it in the center of the microwave. Microwave on high for five seconds. Check the book. If there is no problem caused by microwaving it, give it another five seconds. In time, if the book is placed where it is in contact with fresh air, the smell from the mildew will be minimized. I have done this to books that were kept in a damp environment for about thirty years and now they no longer have an objectionable odor. Another positive result of this technique is it eliminates the factors that give allergic reactions to some people. (I sometimes set the microwave at longer lengths of time than ten seconds, based on my experience on how much time a book can endure without experiencing damage.)

If the book has any bent or folded pages and corners, straighten them and iron them. Use a regular iron on a high or hot setting. Cover each bend to be ironed with a sheet of paper toweling before ironing it. With some practice, one will also be able to determine how much ironing a page can withstand without the protection of the paper towel. It is also possible to remove some crease marks completely by dampening the spot before ironing, but proceed with caution. Do it with minimal water several times rather than allowing the page to become too wet all at once.

Erase any pencil marks inside the book with a kneaded eraser. Never use a pencil eraser, as this causes lifting and roughening of the page. Do not remove inscriptions, such as "To Dickie on his 10th Birthday. Love, Grandma, July 14, 1936," as this gives an old book charm as well as establishes when it was presumably new and is part of its historical provenance. If the original price from a store or the price that a book dealer put in the book is in evidence, leave it, because it is also part of a book's history.

The most valuable part of an old series book is its dust jacket, so special attention is required to preserve it. Most dust jackets were originally varnished to protect them, either entirely or over the front cover picture only. Almost all Grosset & Dunlap books have only the picture varnished, with about 1/8 inch of varnish extended on both sides of the picture. I point this out because the varnished part of the dust jacket can be cleaned more vigorously than the rest of the paper covering, and it is usually the most soiled portion.

To clean the dust jacket, lay it flat on a smooth surface and wipe it off with a paper towel that has been dampened with window cleaner. Do not use too much abrasion or too much fluid, as it can affect the ink on the dust jacket, as well as remove the varnish over the front picture, giving it a streaky effect. Be especially careful of those that are done with red or blue ink as this will wipe off. Another good cleaner for dust jackets (and for picture cover books) is Turtle Wax® Zip Wax®. However, only use this cleaner over a varnished dust jacket.

Many dust jackets have a worse enemy than dirt: tape and price stickers. If the price sticker is an original book price, never remove it. If masking tape or a price sticker is on the jacket from a yard sale, for example, this should be removed. Very carefully. Never, never pull a sticker off a dust jacket, no matter how careful you are, as it almost always causes lifting of the picture surface. Most stickers and tape will loosen enough to remove them cautiously if the area is well heated with a hair dryer. Some transparent tape will also come off this way. To remove the sticky residue left from tape, wipe the area with a paper towel that has been dipped in vegetable oil. (Be very frugal with applying vegetable oil to paper; use it only on non-absorbent paper, such as a varnished dust jacket.) All transparent tape should be removed, as this will discolor the paper in time and spoil the dust jacket. Easier said than done. If the tape will not lift off after it has been heated with a hair dryer or soaked with cigarette lighter fluid (which will not discolor or hurt the dust jacket), it has to stay on.

The next stage in reviving an old book is to iron the clean dust jacket. Lay the dust jacket flat on a hard, smooth surface, such as a kitchen counter, and iron it with a reasonably hot iron, placing a piece of paper towel between the iron and the dust jacket. Never iron directly on the dust jacket, as it will pucker up and the iron may stick to it. This ironing process is especially important for dust jackets on books that have been lying flat with other books piled on top of them, causing the paper from the dust jacket to conform to the contours of the book and to become weak from pressure.

Minor tears or "chips" on a dust jacket should be left alone. If a tear is major or if the dust jacket is in danger of separating into two or more pieces, it should be mended. The tear should never be closed with transparent tape or any other tape (unless one uses professional, non-acidic book tape), as it stains the paper of the dust jacket and becomes brittle with time. The method I use to close tears is to cut strips of acid-free paper about the width of a piece of transparent tape, or wider if necessary, and apply them with glue from a glue stick (on the back side, or course). This is using the restoration method of not applying anything that could not be safely removed again.

The final stage in preservation and protection is to cover the dust jacket with an acid-free polyester cover. These cost about $1.00 per book if purchased separately. If a collector has many books to cover it is more cost-effective to order a roll of this material. Look on the back of one of these covers to see the name and address of the distributor and call him directly. For about $40.00 a roll, one can do about 300 books. The scraps of paper backing left over from the cover are perfect for making mending strips for dust jackets, as they are acid-free.

After all this restoration and preparation, use common sense in shelving and displaying books. Never let direct sunlight fall on the spines of books as this will fade them almost "overnight." Do not pile books up or put things on top of them when they are shelved as this will cause stress and damage the spines. Keep books out of a damp or humid environment, as this is one of their worst enemies. With minimal precaution, your books will last longer than you.

# Common Abbreviations and Terms

| | |
|---|---|
| **Digest** | A paperback book that is about the same size as most series books. (about 5in. X 7in.) |
| **DJ; djs** | The protective paper dust jacket on a book. |
| **Wrap DJ** | The picture on the front of the dust jacket wraps around the spine of the book and is part of it. |
| **EP; eps** | Endpapers on a book. One side is glued to the hard cover; the other is the first "page" of the book. The eps are usually decorative. |
| **Frontis** | The frontispiece is the first, and often only, illustration in a book. |
| **Glossy frontis** | A frontispiece printed on thick, glossy paper. These were hand-tipped into books up until World War II. |
| **Plain frontis** | The frontispiece is printed on the same paper as the rest of the book and is usually a line drawing, like the pictures in coloring books. |
| **Internals** | The illustrations inside a series book, usually placed at equal intervals throughout the text. They were usually glossy and had to be hand-tipped in, like the glossy frontis, and were used mostly before World War II. |
| **Mass-market** | This refers to the common size paperback book, which is usually about 4in. X 6in. |
| **PB** | A paperback book. |
| **PC** | A picture cover book. The picture is printed as part of the covering over the composition or cardboard that makes up the hard covers of the book. Some PCs are made as part of the book; others have a layer of cellophane (which can become loose) over the picture. |

# What Are Girls' Series Books?

Girls' Series Books are book sets in which more than one volume is about the same characters and the stories are meant to appeal primarily to young girls, or young women, of about ten to fifteen years old. The sets contain anywhere from two volumes to well over one hundred volumes.

Series books for juveniles owe part of their origin to the "dime novels" of the late 19th century. These short, cheaply produced books were meant for popular adult entertainment and were adventure stories and detective stories. Another antecedent of the popular Series Books of the 20th century was the "rags to riches" books for boys by Horatio Alger. Alger wrote dozens of volumes of books about poor boys who rose to success through hard work and belief in American ideals. The first was *Ragged Dick, or Life on the Streets* in 1867. This tale was so successful that Alger spent the rest of his life duplicating the pattern, which was enormously popular for the rest of the century and well into the 20th century. The "Alger hero" became an American literary term.

Edward Stratemeyer deserves the credit he gets for inventing the modern concept of juvenile series fiction, beginning with all the books he wrote for boys starting in the last part of the 19th century and which continues today with the Hardy Boys and Nancy Drew series. (See Chapter II, **Ruth Fielding**.) The early Stratemeyer Syndicate books concentrated on reading material for boys, but two years before his first big success, *Under Dewey at Manila*, was published in 1898, Annie Fellows Johnston's *The Little Colonel* was released, which was about a little Southern girl named Lloyd. The Stratemeyer and Johnston books seem xenophobic, racist, offensive and anachronistic today, but they must be judged against the standards of their own times rather than against contemporary values. In 1896 it was not considered unnatural for a wealthy little girl in Kentucky to order around black servants who spoke in dialect and to travel to Europe for further adventures. The Little Colonel had a northern Civil War-inspired counterpart in Dorothy Dale, called "the Little Captain." This was the first Stratemeyer series of books for girls. There were thirteen volumes in the Dorothy Dale books by "Margaret Penrose" from 1908 to 1924.

The first really successful girls' series was Ruth Fielding by Alice B. Emerson, another Stratemeyer pseudonym. This one set the pattern for the popular girls' series that followed as Ruth got into the mystery solving business at the beginning of the series. The most important girls' series books, and the ones that are the most highly sought and collected today, involve girl detectives. This way the story can combine romance, adventure and mystery, offering as many popular fiction genres in one volume as possible.

There were scores of girls' series books available all during the 20th century from several different publishers. The most popular ones were always from Grosset & Dunlap and most of these were Stratemeyer books, such as the Outdoor Girls, the Blythe Girls, the Dana Girls and Nancy Drew. The most important non-Stratemeyer series for Grosset & Dunlap were Judy Bolton, Beverly Gray (who began life with A.L. Burt), Cherry Ames, Vicki Barr and Connie Blair. Cupples & Leon gave us Ruth Fielding, Betty Gordon and Kay Tracey, all Stratemeyer products, and Penny Parker by Mildred A. Wirt, a Stratemeyer writer. Other publishers addressing the juvenile market had scores of series books, but none had the enduring quality or the popularity of the above-mentioned, with the possible exception of Whitman's Trixie Belden.

It is commonly believed that series books are not popular nor are they available for today's youth. This is not true at all. The books stores in the malls are full of them. True, they are not the quality products of the 1930s, but they are there in great abundance in paperback form, especially the new Nancy Drew books. It is even possible that someday they may be collectible.

The classic girls' series sets began to decline with the paper shortages of the World War II era, and more importantly with changes in public (including juvenile) taste in the years following World War II, although there now are undoubtedly more books sold to juveniles than ever before in history. The newer series books do not seem to have the permanent importance they did in the past, but that is for another generation of readers to decide in the future.

What is it that makes certain girls' series books so desirable as collectibles today? One **huge** factor is that they have to have been appreciated by both girls and boys. (How many people collect Little Colonel books?) And this means that they have to be collected by **both** women and men at the present time. They have to have some universal quality of acceptance about them to be still so desirable. Remember, series books are not collected only for display purposes. They can also be read! And enjoyed. (It would be interesting to know the ratio of boys who also read Nancy Drew and girls who also read the Hardy Boys.) The heroines of girls' series books have to be someone that the authors created as likable personalities whose qualities endure for many generations. Although the Elsie Dinsmore books began in 1868 and must have enjoyed some sort of success, this twenty-eight-volume set is impossible to read today because of its saccharine nature and lack of any real literary value; however, the Elsie books probably did influence 20th-century series books.

Those who collect Judy Bolton books, for example, read them over and over. It is quite certain that those who do this enjoy reading the books and remembering the plot devices and surprises in the mystery stories. Some of these people are "buffs" who know the story better than the author would. They are also reliving their youth and a time when everything was new and the future was full of promise. It is probably true that older people enjoy the past because they have much more of it than they do of the future. But why analyze it? In my own case, and no doubt in that of many other collectors/readers, it is too interesting not to enjoy again and again. (Would one look at the Mona Lisa only once?) There is always the comfort of the known and the trusted.

One has to wonder who decided what the ages of potential readers were for the various series books. On Grosset & Dunlap book dust jackets, a number was given at the bottom for determining the age of the child the book was intended for. The number "80-110" on the Five Little Peppers series meant that the books were for children age eight to eleven. The Nancy Drew books had the number "100-150," meaning ages ten to fifteen. This had to have been based on the subject matter, not the reading level. When I was twelve, I had some problems understanding situations and conversations in the Pepper books; I did not in the Nancy Drew books. Even today I think that the language and style of the Five Little Peppers books is far in advance of an eight-year-old reader. The Beverly Gray number is "120-160." I thought as a child, and I still do, that this series is for adults, not teenagers. After the first four books, all the characters range in age from the mid twenties to the early thirties. All of these books can be enjoyed by adults as much as by young people. The main determining factor of how the Judy Bolton series, also about people in their twenties, is meant for youngsters is that there is never any mention of sexual conduct, overt violence or graphic situations.

Earlier in this chapter it was pointed out that which gives an old book its value. Another element that continues to interest and puzzle collectors of series books is the problem of "First Editions."

All of us who collect the books and look for them on sales lists and on eBay are constantly amused by such common statements as "probable first edition."

This is not an inaccurate statement. It is just terribly redundant. Case in point: The Judy Bolton Mystery, Volume 9, *The Mysterious Half Cat*, is **always** a first edition. There was never any other edition. Every single volume is the same edition. What the seller means is no doubt "First Printing." Who knows? This book was printed from 1936 through at least 1966, many different times. The problem is that many (if not most) of the people who have the book for sale do not understand much about books. If they see a copyright of 1936 on a book they assume that this very copy was printed in 1936, although there are seven distinct formats for *The Mysterious Half Cat* and within each format there are quite a few variations. It is even possible that the book was printed 30 different times during 30 years by Grosset & Dunlap. Thus, series books are also distinct from many other books in that they were printed over and over for years and years. It is a real shame that the publishers did not list the number and the year of the printings on series books as was done on Little Golden Books. (On the other hand, it is bad enough that there are different formats to collect.)

Those who know anything about series books realize that the early format editions and later volumes in any given series are the most difficult ones to find today. Most early volumes were printed over and over. How many times was *The Vanishing Shadow* printed? More than thirty. How many times was *The Secret of the Sand Castle* printed? Only once and in far less quantity than almost any printing of *The Vanishing Shadow*.

A last thought on collecting the sets of series books, as opposed to getting them just to read them: Would we bother to collect them if they were still available in retail outlets in their original presentation just like they were when we were young? Probably.

# Formats

The "Formats" used for each series of books is a way to designate the differences between them. Books and pamphlets have already established Formats for some of these girls' series books, but I have used my own system, which is less complicated than others already in print. I find it easier to do it this way instead of breaking each series down into such specific components that it is difficult to determine some of the minor differences between them. The "Formatting" used here divides each series into differences that are obvious and each is explained for the series that it represents. This formatting system is not meant to contradict others in use; it is meant as an aid in establishing prices for the books and as a way to build uniform collections of a certain series, although that is not always possible either.

# CHAPTER 2

# Ruth Fielding Series

During the early years of the 20th century, the most popular girls' series was Ruth Fielding by Alice B. Emerson, which lasted from 1913 to 1934 and included thirty books. This is the series that was the inspiration for all the others included in this book.

Ruth Fielding was the creation of Edward Stratemeyer. Stratemeyer developed the plot outlines for the books and assigned them to "ghost writers" who filled in the details. W. Bert Foster wrote some of the Ruth Fielding books as "Alice B. Emerson." Lilian Garis, who wrote many of her own books such as the Melody Lane Series, probably had a hand in several of them. The most famous writer who worked from Stratemeyer's Ruth Fielding outlines was Mildred A. Wirt who did volumes 23 though 26 before she concentrated on the new Nancy Drew Series. The Ruth Fielding books were written during the high point in the development of new girls' series. (Carol Billman reports in *The Secret of the Stratemeyer Syndicate* that from 1910 to 1920 there were about ninety-four different girls' series books in progress.)

Ruth began as a poor orphan, a staple of 19th century girls' books. With the "luck and pluck" of an Alger hero, she took on the most popular roles of women in the early 20th century. Ruth became internationally famous as a detective, a scenario writer for the movies, a leading actress, a director and a film company owner. Like many other modern heroines of her time, she attended boarding school and college where she earned many good friends. She also became a wife and mother without giving up her career. No doubt much of the inspiration for this came from Mary Pickford (1893-1979) who was the most famous woman in the world during the same time period as the Ruth Fielding books were written.

"Little Mary," who was the number one film box office attraction for twenty-four years, did all that Ruth did, except that she was not involved in solving mysteries.

One thing that sets Ruth apart from other girl sleuths and series heroines is that she worked hard to accomplish her goals and did not have a loving parent or unlimited funds to help her. In 1927, the year that aviator Charles Lindbergh crossed the Atlantic in The Spirit of St. Louis, Ruth won $50,000 in a movie scenario contest, twice the amount of the Orteig Prize that Lindbergh got for being the first to fly non-stop from New York to Paris.

Probably the reason why the Ruth Fielding series ended is that as Ruth continued to age, her appeal was lost to her readers. Nancy Drew, who was "born" at the time the Ruth Fielding Series was ending, was never plagued with the problem of aging or changing and she has lasted for more than seventy years now.

The Ruth Fielding Series of thirty books never had to endure the indignity of being "updated and modernized," although the books are now far less well-known than Ruth's successors, as her appeal and the situations in which she was involved go back too many generations. It does seem to be a fact of fictional life that a girl detective loses her popularity if her mysteries have a dated quality to them. It is still possible for youngsters to worry about conducting a search for a will that will aid an unfortunate person but it is difficult for them to identify with hunting for a "lost soldier...at the War Front" or dealing with the creation of "Talking Pictures," let alone becoming involved with the internal politics of the "monarchies of Estralia and Bellogia."

## Edward Stratemeyer

Edward Stratemeyer (1862-1930) grew up in the era when Americans were taught that there was no accomplishment to which they could not aspire. The period in American history after the Civil War, especially in the victorious North, was one in which life was changing rapidly as Americans by the thousands left the countryside to move to the cities where opportunities were limitless. It was the age of Carnegie, Rockefeller, Morgan and many others who made it big in a big way. It was the era in which Horatio Alger wrote dozens of books proving how "living right paid off." At least it seemed this way, and

Stratemeyer must have believed it was. He did not become successful with iron and steel, oil or finance; he did become the most prolific American writer and/or book producer of all time. Yet he was never blamed for creating a monopoly, as were the "robber barons" of the era.

Stratemeyer, who had only an eighth-grade education, was a voracious reader of the juvenile literature of his time. Imitating the popular works he preferred, he wrote and published his first story in the boys' magazine *Golden Days* in 1889, for which he received $75, a goodly amount of money then. He was later hired by Street and Smith, publishers of dime novels and fiction magazines, where he met his childhood idols, Oliver Optic and Horatio Alger, Jr., the authors of the "living right pays off" juvenile novels he read as a youth. At Street and Smith, Stratemeyer edited and finished the books Alger and Optic had not completed at the time of their deaths and he also wrote at least eleven new volumes under the Alger name.

From 1894 to 1908, Stratemeyer wrote about seventy-five boys' books in several different series and these were published under his own name by various companies that concentrated on the juvenile market, such as Lothrop, Lee & Shephard. These books were about boys and their adventures, success stories of the Alger type and patriotic volumes dealing with American bravery in the Revolution and other wars. The most successful of these books was *Under Dewey at Manila*, published in 1898 at the time of the American victory over Spain in a brief and popular war.

Around 1906, Stratemeyer formed a syndicate to complete all the book ideas he was developing. It is estimated that he personally wrote about 200 books and that he outlined and edited another few hundred that were finished by ghostwriters. The most popular of these were Tom Swift, the Rover Boys, the Bobbsey Twins, Baseball Joe, the Outdoor Girls, Ruth Fielding, Honey Bunch, Bomba the Jungle Boy, Nancy Drew and the Hardy Boys. Stratemeyer created many pen names for the "authors" of these series books. Many of the names had obvious meanings, such as Arthur M. Winfield, the "author" of the Rover Boys books. Arthur is a homonym for author, "M" is for the millions (of books or dollars) hoped for and "Winfield" stood for success.

No one person could produce all the books Stratemeyer had in mind so he hired writers who finished books that he plotted and outlined and they were published under "house names." A good example of this is Laura Lee Hope, author of the Bobbsey Twins books, the longest running Stratemeyer series, which was published from 1904 until very recently. Many different writers worked on this list and on "Miss Hope's" other works, such as the Six Little Bunkers, the Outdoor Girls and the Moving Picture Girls. Ghostwriters who filled in the details of the stories were paid a flat rate of about $75 to $100 (some writers probably commanded more) for each completed 200-page book. Lately there has been a great number of articles and books decrying the practice of paying the ghostwriters so little. How long would it require to write a Bobbsey Twins book in 1925? Two weeks? A month? At any rate, the number of words in the book was less than the average newspaper reporter wrote in a week for a salary of about $20 per week. A certain amount of talent and imagination was required to fill in the details of a Stratemeyer Syndicate book, but the real credit does seem to belong to Edward Stratemeyer and his successors who provided most of the creativity.

Some of the most important Stratemeyer writers were the ones who worked on the three most enduring series. These are Howard R. Garis who wrote about twenty-five Bobbsey Twins books and thirty-five Tom Swift ones; Mildred A. Wirt who created several of the Ruth Fielding, Nancy Drew and Kay Tracey books; and Leslie McFarlane who did the Hardy Boys books for the first twenty years. The identities of these authors were kept secret (by contract) for most of the 20th century.

Another Stratemeyer invention was the 50-cent book. In 1906, a Five Little Peppers book from Lothrop, Lee & Shepard cost $1.50; other publishers' juvenile series were priced about the same. Cupples & Leon's and Grosset & Dunlap's 50-cent Stratemeyer books had heavy cloth-covered covers, a full color dust jacket, from one to four internal illustrations, heavy acid-free paper and clear typesetting with large print. None of these books was considered "literature" by librarians and they were not found in public libraries until very recently. This factor probably caused more books to be sold than anything else, as young people loved them and wanted to read them. The volume of old copies still available for collectors proves that many millions were printed. All of the Stratemeyer Syndicate books showed several generations of juveniles a positive, affirmative and enthusiastic view of American life. They always gave hope for a promising future and, like Alger's books, proved that "living right pays." It is true that there were racial and ethnic stereotypes in the books, but there were probably less than in adult fiction of the same period.

The Stratemeyer Syndicate supplied the publishing houses that catered to the juvenile market, such as Cupples & Leon and Grosset & Dunlap, with product during the entire 20th century. Mr. Stratemeyer was always astute in designing new series books and addressed the popular adult trends by creating a similar juvenile market. Examples of this are Bomba the Jungle Boy, an obvious Tarzan-type; all the "Moving Picture" series of the period in which the movies were developing as popular entertainment; and the teenage detectives like Nancy Drew and the Hardys who were introduced at the time of rising popularity in adult detective fiction.

When Stratemeyer died in 1930, his daughters, Harriet Stratemeyer Adams and Edna Stratemeyer Squier, continued with his work and the Stratemeyer Syndicate, consolidating the policies begun by their father.

# Early Series Books by Edward Stratemeyer

| Series | Dates | Volumes |
|---|---|---|
| Bound to Succeed | 1894-1899 | 3 |
| Ship and Shore | 1894-1900 | 3 |
| Bound to Win | 1897 | 12 |
| Working Upwards | 1897 | 4 |
| Minute Boys | 1898-1912 | 11 |
| Old Glory | 1898-1901 | 6 |
| Soldiers of Fortune | 1900-1906 | 4 |
| American Boys Biographical | 1901-1904 | 2 |
| Colonial (French & Indian War) | 1901-1906 | 6 |
| Pan-American | 1902-1911 | 6 |
| Great American Industries | 1903 | 1 |
| Dave Porter | 1905-1919 | 15 |
| Lakeport | 1908-1912 | 6 |

# Stratemeyer Series by Pseudonyms and Ghostwriters

| Series | Author | Dates | Volumes |
|---|---|---|---|
| Young Sportsmen | Capt. Ralph Bonehill | 1897 | 3 |
| Flag of Freedom | Capt. Ralph Bonehill | 1899-1902 | 6 |
| Rover Boys | Arthur M. Winfield | 1899-1926 | 30 |
| Young Hunters | Capt. Ralph Bonehill | 1900 | 2 |
| Mexican War Series | Capt. Ralph Bonehill | 1900-1902 | 3 |
| Putnam Hall | Arthur M. Winfield | 1901-1911; 1921 | 6 |
| Frontier Series | Capt. Ralph Bonehill | 1903-1906 | 3 |
| Bobbsey Twins | Laura Lee Hope | 1904+ | 72+ |
| Deep Sea | Roy Rockwood | 1905-1908 | 4 |
| Dave Fearless | Roy Rockwood | 1905-1927 | 17 |
| Boy Hunters | Capt. Ralph Bonehill | 1906-1910 | 4 |
| Boys of Business | Allen Chapman | 1906-1911 | 5 |
| Motor Boys | Clarence Young | 1906-1924 | 22 |
| Ralph (Railroad) | Allen Chapman | 1906-1928 | 10 |
| Great Marvel | Roy Rockwood | 1906-1935 | 9 |
| Jack Ranger | Clarence Young | 1907-1911 | 6 |
| Darewell Chums | Allen Chapman | 1908-1911 | 5 |
| Dorothy Dale | Margaret Penrose | 1908-1924 | 13 |
| The Webster Series | Frank V. Webster | 1909-1915; 1938 | 25 |
| College Sports | Lester Chadwick | 1910-1913 | 6 |
| Motor Girls | Margaret Penrose | 1910-1917 | 10 |
| Tom Swift | Victor Appleton | 1910-1941 | 40 |
| Boys of Columbia High | Graham B. Forbes | 1911-1920 | 8 |
| Racer Boys | Clarence Young | 1912-1914 | 6 |
| Fairview Boys | Frederick Gordon | 1912-1917 | 6 |

| Series | Author | Dates | Volumes |
|---|---|---|---|
| Baseball Joe | Lester Chadwick | 1912-1928 | 14 |
| Fred Fenton | Allen Chapman | 1913-1915 | 5 |
| Dave Dashaway | Roy Rockwood | 1913-1915 | 5 |
| Tom Fairfield | Allen Chapman | 1913-1915 | 5 |
| Motion Picture Chums | Victor Appleton | 1913-1916 | 7 |
| Moving Picture Boys | Victor Appleton | 1913-1922 | 10 |
| Outdoor Girls | Laura Lee Hope | 1913-1933 | 23 |
| Ruth Fielding | Alice B. Emerson | 1913-1934 | 30 |
| Speedwell Boys | Roy Rockwood | 1913-1915 | 5 |
| Moving Picture Girls | Laura Lee Hope | 1914-1916 | 7 |
| Corner House Girls | Grace Brooks Hill | 1915-1926 | 13 |
| White Ribbon Boys | Raymond Sperry, Jr. | 1915 | ? |
| Bunny Brown and His Sister Sue | Laura Lee Hope | 1916-1931 | ? |
| Nan Sherwood | Annie Roe Carr | 1916-1937 | 7 |
| Six Little Bunkers | Laura Lee Hope | 1918-1930 | ? |
| Betty Gordon | Alice B. Emerson | 1920-1932 | 15 |
| Billie Bradley | Janet D. Wheeler | 1920-1932 | 9 |
| Make-Believe Stories | Laura Lee Hope | 1920-1923 | 12+(?) |
| Four Little Blossoms | Mabel C. Hawley | 1920-1930; 1938 | ? |
| Radio Boys | Allen Chapman | 1922-1930 | 13 |
| Radio Girls | Margaret Penrose | 1922-1924 | 4 |
| Honey Bunch | Helen Louise Thorndyke | 1923-1955 | 32 |
| Blythe Girls | Laura Lee Hope | 1925-1932 | 12 |
| Don Sturdy | Victor Appleton | 1925-1935 | 15 |
| Flyaways | Alice Dale Hardy | 1925 | ? |
| The X-Bar-X Boys | James Cody Ferris | 1926-1942 | 22 |
| Bomba the Jungle Boy | Roy Rockwood | 1926-1928; 1953 | 20 |
| Frank Allen | Graham B. Forbes | 1926-1927 | 17 |
| Hardy Boys | Franklin W. Dixon | 1927+ | 100+ |
| Ted Scott | Franklin W. Dixon | 1927-1943 | 20 |
| Nancy Drew | Carolyn Keene | 1930+ | 100+ |
| Doris Force | Julia K. Duncan | 1931-1932 | 4 |
| Dana Girls | Carolyn Keene | 1934-1979 | 34 |
| Kay Tracey | Frances K. Judd | 1934-1942; 1951-1953; 1978; 1980 | 18 |
| Happy Hollisters | Jerry West | 1953-1970; 1979 | 33 |
| Tom Swift, Jr. | Victor Appleton II | 1954-1971 | 33 |
| Honey Bunch and Norman | Helen Louise Thorndyke | 1957-1963 | 12 |
| Bret King | Dan Scott | 1960-1964 | 9 |
| Linda Craig | Ann Sheldon | 1962-1964; 1981; 1988-1990 | 11 / 12 |
| Christopher Cool TEEN Agent | Jack Lancer | 1967-1969 | 6 |
| Tolliver Adventure Series | Alan Stone | 1967 | 3 |
| Tom Swift (III) | Victor Appleton III | 1981-1984 | 11 |

# Mildred A. Wirt Benson

The most famous writer who worked on the Ruth Fielding books was Mildred A. Wirt Benson. Benson still writes for *The Blade*, the daily newspaper in Toledo, Ohio. She was born Mildred Augustine in Ladora, Iowa, in 1905. She met Edward Stratemeyer in New York in 1925 and began working for his syndicate as a writer who fleshed out his plot outlines for juvenile mystery stories. In 1929, she began to write Stratemeyer's Nancy Drew Mystery Stories for a reported $125.00 per book. In 1950, three years after her husband Asa Wirt died, she married George Benson, the editor of *The Toledo Times,* from which point her professional career was focused on newspaper writing.

Mrs. Benson reportedly gained her first series book writing experience with Volumes 23 to 26 of the Ruth Fielding Series. She wrote twenty-three of the Nancy Drew books and several Dana Girls and Kay Tracey books, all for the Stratemeyer Syndicate. Under her own name, she wrote many other series, such as the Brownie Scouts, Penny Nichols, Penny Parker, and the most unusual to carry the by-line of a woman writer, the six Dan Carter Cub Scouts books for boys.

The Stratemeyer Syndicate did not reveal the names of the actual authors of the Nancy Drew books until after Harriet Stratemeyer Adams' death in 1982. By the 1990s, the Nancy Drew books that Mrs. Benson wrote for the Stratemeyer Syndicate carried this notice: "Acknowledgement is made to Mildred Wirt Benson, who under the pen name Carolyn Keene, wrote the original NANCY DREW books."

Mildred Wirt Benson deserves much credit for her work for the Stratemeyer Syndicate, especially

Mildred A. Wirt Benson. The Blade *photograph by Diane Hires.*

for the Nancy Drew books because of their great success after she developed much of their apparent character. In an interview for *People Magazine* in December 1998, Benson showed her impatience with silly questions and the fuss made about her authorship of Nancy Drew but apparently she still values her own worth as a writer and creator of fiction and is aware of her importance in the history of series literature.

# Ruth Fielding Illustrators

There are only four different dust jacket designs for the thirty Ruth Fielding books, but several different illustrators did the frontispieces inside the books, including W.S. Rogers, R. Emmett Owen, Thelma Gooch, Bess Goe Willis and Russell H. Tandy.

Russell H. Tandy (1893-1961) painted dust jackets for many juvenile series books from 1929 to 1949. For Cupples & Leon, he did the Peggy Lee Stories for Girls, the Buddy Series by Howard R. Garis and the frontispieces for the last three Ruth Fielding books. For Grosset & Dunlap, he painted the dust jackets and the internals for the first twenty-six Nancy Drew books (except for the dust jacket on Volume 11) and many dust jackets and frontispieces for Beverly Gray and Hardy Boys books. His color work is noted for the strong primary colors of his palette and the absence of weak pastel shading. His signature is always prominently featured on his artwork.

Clara M. Burd (1873-1933) did the "Wall" dust jacket of the Ruth Fielding series. She is probably the most important 20th century illustrator whose paintings appear on series books. Much of her work is signed "CMB" or "C.M. Burd," which has often confused her with English illustrator Cicely Mary Barker. Burd's beautiful watercolors have a strong three-dimensional effect because of the manner in which she outlined her figures. Among her many book illustrations are the ones done for the John C. Winston Company's Louisa May Alcott books and for other classics, such as *Heidi* and *Hans Brinker*. The poignant children in several versions of Robert Louis Stevenson's *A Child's Garden of Verses* for Saalfield, from the 1920s through the 1940s, are among her best work. She also did a huge quantity of religious paintings that were used for Sunday School diplomas and post cards, most of them featuring small children. The people in Burd's work appear to be from the 19th century, which is the reason I like them so much. For the first third of the 20th century her work was featured on every conceivable type of item that required illustrations, from bread wrappers to popular magazine covers, and she also did stained glass designs for Tiffany's.

# The Ruth Fielding Books

All the Ruth Fielding books were published by Cupples & Leon in "thick" editions with a spine of about 1¼ inches wide. They all have good cloth covers, thick pages and a glossy frontispiece. These frontispiece pictures were printed on glossy paper so the reproduction quality would be better than if they were done on the paper of the text pages and they were hand-inserted into the books. Many series books of the 1930s included up to four of these pictures in them. And, at this time, the books cost 50 cents each, which was a bargain even then.

There are two distinct types of hard tan covers on the Ruth Fielding books. The first is an early 20th century scene of Ruth sitting beside a creek bank and holding an open book. She is wearing a long "sailor-type" dress. The second cover is from 1929 and it shows the same scene in an updated version in which Ruth wears a short-skirted dress. The earlier picture has red highlights in it; the second version does not.

There are four different dust jacket designs on the Ruth Fielding books and all of them are alike for the set that they represent, except that the title is changed for the proper volume in the series. The four dust jacket designs became progressively more sophisticated as they were updated.

**Jacket #1, "Plain creek bank."** This is the same scene as the hard cover of 1913 to 1929. The paper stock is heavier than any later covers.

**Jacket #2, "Color creek bank."** For the second set of dust jackets, the first one was redrawn and painted in color with a full background showing the creek bank more clearly. In many ways, the revised pose of Ruth is stiffer looking than the plainer picture, which can be noted in the awkward way in which she holds her book. Ruth Fielding expert Kenneth Hopping places this jacket as beginning in 1918.

**Jacket #3, "Wall."** Ruth is standing in front of a high stone wall and wearing a long red cape. The costume that she wears in this Clara M. Burd illustration from 1926 seems even more old-fashioned than the early "creek bank" dresses, but I like it best because Ruth seems so young and innocent and I am a great fan of Clara M. Burd art.

**Jacket #4, "Collage."** The 1929 dust jacket shows a portrait of Ruth with short, bobbed hair surrounded by eight scenes from her life, including a hand-cranked motion picture camera photographing her. This dust jacket is colorful and interesting and it must have looked very modern in 1929. I wish that we knew who painted it.

Dust Jacket Style #4 is the only one in which an entire set of Ruth Fielding books potentially could be collected in a uniform format. It was not unusual at the time of the Ruth Fielding books to present an entire series with a single dust jacket picture. The Buddy Series from Cupples & Leon was done this way and the Bobbsey Twins books from Grosset & Dunlap had the same picture on each dust jacket in the set for years, although they were updated many times like the Ruth Fielding dust jackets.

Most of the Ruth Fielding books have secondary titles that help to explain more about the theme or plot of the book. This was a common manner of titling mystery and series books in the early years of the 20th century. Only the main title appears on the covers and dust jackets of the books. The "subtitle" is listed on the title page and on some lists inside the books and on some of the flaps of the dust jackets. An example of this is: *Ruth Fielding at Silver Ranch Or Schoolgirls Among the Cowboys.* (There are variations of punctuation and capitalization in dealing with the "Or.")

## RUTH FIELDING BOOK FORMATS

**Cupples & Leon Co.**

I.  1913 - 1918
    Thick tan cover w/1913 scene
    The dj repeats the hard cover picture
    "Plain creek bank" dj
    Glossy frontis
    Good paper

II. 1918 - 1925
    Same tan cover as Format I
    Full color, full scene dj
    "Color creek bank" dj
    Glossy frontis
    Good paper

III. 1926 - 1928.
     Same tan cover as Format I
     "Wall" dj
     Glossy frontis
     Good paper

IV. 1929 - 1934
    Thick tan cover w/1920s scene
    "Collage" dj
    Glossy frontis
    Good paper

## RUTH FIELDING BOOK VALUES

Values for Ruth Fielding books fall mostly within their format categories. It is more difficult to find Format I books in very good condition than it is to locate Format IV books that way.

| | |
|---|---|
| Format I | $3.00 - $22.00 |
| Format II | $3.00 - $20.00 |
| Format III | $3.00 - $20.00 |
| Format IV | $3.00 - $20.00 |

**Exception:** Format IV, Volumes 23 - 30
$3.00 - $30.00+

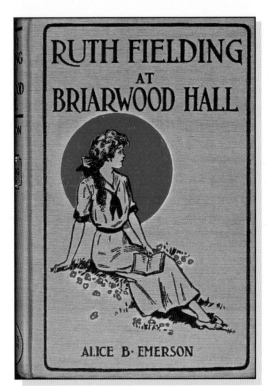

Front Cover A. 1913-1929.

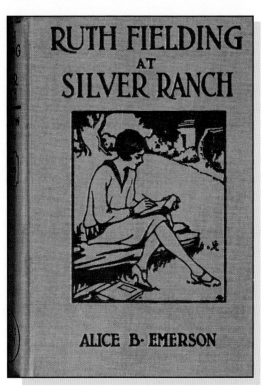

Front Cover B. 1929-1934.

## 1. Ruth Fielding of the Red Mill or Jasper Parloe's Secret

1913 Edition. 204 Pages.

Ruth as a 12-year-old orphan is sent to live with her great-uncle at Red Mill. She becomes friends with Helen Cameron and her brother, Tom. There is a dam break and flood in which Ruth saves the uncle's money. Her reward is boarding school with Helen.

## 2. Ruth Fielding at Briarwood Hall or Solving the Campus Mystery

1913 Edition. 206 Pages.

Ruth solves a campus mystery involving a marble harp and a ghost.

## 3. Ruth Fielding at Snow Camp or Lost in the Backwoods

1913 Edition. 204 Pages.

On a winter vacation Ruth solves the mystery involving a boy who keeps disappearing.

## 4. Ruth Fielding at Lighthouse Point or Nita, the Girl Castaway

1913 Edition. 202 Pages.

Another vacation and mystery, this time on the Atlantic coast.

## 5. Ruth Fielding at Silver Ranch or Schoolgirls Among the Cowboys

1913 Edition. 204 Pages.

Ruth and her friends vacation in Montana where Ruth recovers money for her uncle again.

## 6. Ruth Fielding on Cliff Island or The Old Hunter's Treasure Box

1915 Edition. 202 Pages.

Ruth and her friends travel to Cliff Island where a real estate mystery is solved.

## 7. Ruth Fielding at Sunrise Farm or What Became of the Raby Orphans

1915 Edition. 204 Pages.

Ruth and her friends help orphaned siblings reunite and Helen makes the discovery that "when we go anywhere with you, Ruth…you always take your 'good times' with you."

## 8. Ruth Fielding and the Gypsies or The Missing Pearl Necklace

1915 Edition. 204 Pages.

Ruth (like her later counterparts Nancy Drew and Beverly Gray) is kidnapped by Gypsies. She solves the mystery of a missing necklace, for which she is rewarded with $5,000.

## 9. Ruth Fielding in Moving Pictures or Helping the Dormitory Fund

1916 Edition. 208 Pages.

A dormitory at Briarwood burns down (like Beverly Gray's did later) and Ruth makes a movie to raise money to build a new one. She graduates.

## 10. Ruth Fielding Down in Dixie or Great Times in the Land of Cotton

1916 Edition. 206 Pages.

Ruth and Helen visit South Carolina and are involved in local problems.

**11. Ruth Fielding at College or The Missing Examination Papers**

1917 Edition. 206 Pages.

Ruth and Helen go to Ardmore College and solve the mystery of a valuable vase that was stolen. (Guess what was in it?)

**12. Ruth Fielding in the Saddle or College Girls in the Land of Gold**

1917 Edition. 208 Pages.

Ruth goes to California to make another movie and also discovers gold.

**13. Ruth Fielding in the Red Cross or Doing Her Best for Uncle Sam**

1918 Edition. 204 Pages.

What was happening in Europe in 1918? Ruth, Helen, Jennie and Tom all go to France "to make the world safe for Democracy."

**14. Ruth Fielding at the War Front or The Hunt for the Lost Soldier**

1918 Edition. 204 Pages.

Tom is missing behind enemy lines and Ruth goes looking for him. Ruth who "knows the mind of the Hun" watches "our brave boys in khaki...hold the German horde back." Tom is located and he shows the girls "the big shell holes—and all."

**15. Ruth Fielding Homeward Bound or A Red Cross Worker's Ocean Perils**

1919 Edition. 210 Pages.

Ruth braves Zeppelins with a broken shoulder to return home to help her aunt and uncle.

DJ #1

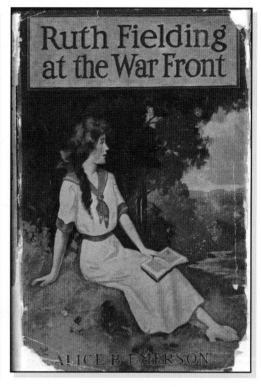

DJ #2

**16. Ruth Fielding Down East or The Hermit of Beach Plum Point**

1920 Edition. 208 Pages.

Ruth writes a movie scenario that is stolen. Tom returns to France.

**17. Ruth Fielding in the Great Northwest or The Indian Girl Star of the Movies**

1921 Edition. 206 Pages.

Ruth, Helen and Jennie are in the West making a movie. Tom wants Ruth to marry him.

**18. Ruth Fielding on the St. Lawrence or The Queer Old Man of the Thousand Islands**

1922 Edition. 208 Pages.

Ruth has adventures in the same territory as Judy Bolton did in *The Ghost Parade.*

**19. Ruth Fielding Treasure Hunting or A Moving Picture That Became Real**

1923 Edition. 210 Pages.

Ruth, with the help of Tom, goes to the Bahamas to make a movie.

**20. Ruth Fielding in the Far North or The Lost Motion Picture Company**

1924 Edition. 206 Pages.

Ruth travels to the Arctic to film her own scenario and face many dangers.

**21. Ruth Fielding at Golden Pass or The Perils of an Artificial Avalanche**

1925 Edition. 205 Pages.

Ruth and Tom travel to Montana to film another of Ruth's scenarios. When she loses her leading actress, she becomes the star of the picture.

DJ #3

DJ #4

### 22. Ruth Fielding in Alaska or The Girl Miners of Snow Mountain

1926 Edition. 210 Pages.

Ruth solves the mystery of who stole the film from scenes completed in Alaska.

### 23. Ruth Fielding and Her Great Scenario or Striving for the Motion Picture Prize

1927 Edition. 208 Pages.

The Fielding Film Company and all Ruth's friends travel to the Maine coast to complete another movie. A scenario that Ruth had planned to enter in a contest is stolen but ultimately restored to her and she "defeated hundreds of the best scenario writers from every country in the world" to win the $50,000 prize. No wonder "Tom lifted her off the ground, kissing her twice."

### 24. Ruth Fielding at Cameron Hall or A Mysterious Disappearance

1928 Edition. 210 Pages.

Ruth helps Tom prove that he is innocent of a bank robbery and then marries him, as he is willing to allow her to pursue her film career and retain her maiden name.

### 25. Ruth Fielding Clearing Her Name or The Rivals of Hollywood

1929 Edition. 210 Pages.

Ruth must prove that the person who accused her of not writing a prize-winning scenario is lying. She restores her reputation in Hollywood.

### 26. Ruth Fielding in Talking Pictures or The Prisoners of the Tower

1930 Edition. 208 Pages.

Ruth and Helen are kidnapped and taken to Mexico as prisoners of troubled Mexican actor Ortiz Coronada. (A juvenile series book about the "Talkies" became dated very quickly.)

### 27. Ruth Fielding and Baby June

1931 Edition. 210 Pages.

Now Ortiz Coronada is accused of kidnapping Ruth's baby daughter.

### 28. Ruth Fielding and Her Double

1932 Edition. 204 Pages.

Once Baby June is securely settled at Red Mill, Ruth and Helen return to Hollywood to solve the mystery of an actress who is presenting herself as Ruth Fielding Cameron.

### 29. Ruth Fielding and Her Greatest Triumph or Saving Her Company from Disaster

1933 Edition. 202 Pages.

Ruth makes her most acclaimed film, which is about a South Seas island romance, although a rival attempts to make the same picture first.

### 30. Ruth Fielding and Her Crowning Victory or Winning Honors Abroad

1934 Edition. 210 Pages.

This is the most unbelievable of all Ruth Fielding stories. Ruth and Helen travel to Europe without their husbands and babies and become involved in the problems of warring Bellogia and Estralia. Ruth is given the title Duchess of Sharlot for her part in restoring Prince Robin to the throne. End of series.

# CHAPTER 3

# Nancy Drew Mystery Stories

Many writers of popular culture have speculated about the success of the Nancy Drew series. It is the longest enduring girls' series by many years. The first mystery, *The Secret of the Old Clock*, was first published seventy years ago. The closest competitor in both years and popularity, Judy Bolton, lasted thirty-five years. This study concentrates only on the "Classic Nancy Drew Mysteries," as the ones written since the last new hardback from Grosset & Dunlap (1979) have strayed farther and farther from the series conceived by Edward Stratemeyer and now bear only slight resemblance to the original volumes of the set. The series had to change to appeal to today's young readers, since it is and always was written to make money, not to establish literary precedents or to make artistic statements, but the Classic books are more desired by adult collectors.

The fact that the Nancy Drew books were attractively designed and priced also helped greatly with their success. The art on the dust jackets was always eye catching, especially so with the books up to the late 1940s with covers by R.H. Tandy whose palette was dominated by primary colors and who painted vivid scenes that "told a story." In 1930, when the series began, each volume cost 50 cents; by 1950, they were 75 cents; and, in the year 2000, the Classic hard cover volumes are less than $5.00. It is estimated that about 100 million Nancy Drew books have been sold in the past seventy years.

Supposedly the reason that the series has had so much appeal for young readers, especially girls, is because Nancy was mostly permitted to do as she pleased. The early books in the series state that Nancy is sixteen years old, yet there were never stories dealing with school life or school problems. Nancy is completely independent. Her father, Attorney Carson Drew, has no rules for her to follow, but it is also assumed that Nancy would only conduct herself properly anyhow. Housekeeper Hannah Gruen has no authority over the young detective either. Nancy has her own car; she dresses nicely; she has wonderful friends who all defer to her judgment; she is never afraid no matter how potentially dangerous the situation is; she is more clever than most adults and can translate ancient texts as well as tap dance in Morse code; and Nancy is very pretty.

Right from the beginning, the Nancy Drew books were fast-paced and exciting and each chapter ended in a situation that demanded quick page turning. Nancy's mystery solving was almost always for the purpose of helping a person who had very little other recourse to aid, or who could not afford it. Those she aided the most were innocent young girls or pathetic elderly persons, examples being poor little Judy of Volume 1, *The Secret of the Old Clock*, and the aged Trumbull sisters in Volume 2, *The Hidden Staircase*.

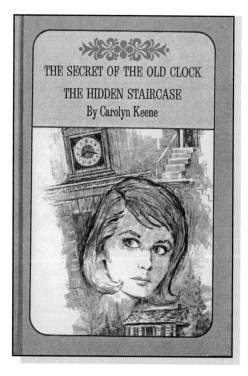

Nancy Drew "Twin Thriller," 1970s.

Many of Nancy's mysteries involved going on vacations with her friends Bess and George, and these trips were usually to some exotic locale that young women their age would never visit, such as dude ranches, remote inns, resorts and such in the early books, and places like Scotland, France, Africa and Peru in the later volumes of the Classic series. Nancy got around even more than world traveler Beverly Gray who was much older than she.

The Nancy Drew series at its inception was probably conceived as just another girls' series that updated the problems encountered by former protagonists of Stratemeyer Syndicate books, such as schoolgirl and later movie maker Ruth Fielding. But by 1930, Edward Stratemeyer had years of experience as to what it took to make a series successful and the first hired writer who filled in his plot outlines, Mildred Wirt, was more experienced with the ghostwriting business and more imaginative in fleshing out Mr. Stratemeyer's and his daughters' outlines than other Syndicate writers would have been. One of the most clever elements of the series was that Nancy never aged or changed, except that in the updated versions of the books in the 1950s, she became eighteen instead of sixteen, primarily because a young lady of sixteen in the 1950s would not have been able to conduct herself as independently as Nancy still did.

The "updated" books were also shortened and speeded up in pace. They were modernized in that they eliminated the racial and ethnic stereotypes

CAROLYN KEENE

PASSWORD TO LARKSPUR LANE

NANCY DREW MYSTERY NO 12

Armada paperback, England, 1980.

that were found in all fiction, including that written for adults, in the early years of the 20th century. And, most of all, they were geared to a younger audience than they had been in the 1930s and 1940s. By the late 1950s, series books had to compete with movies and television as entertainment for young people. Also, economics and not the "shorter attention spans" that readers of Nancy Drew books were accused of having, caused other changes. It is less expensive to produce a 180-page book than a 210-page one.

Probably the one factor that permitted Nancy Drew to reign as queen of all series books for so long is that the books carefully blended fantasy and reality in such a way that they were exciting to read and still believable in spite of all the criticism that could be leveled at their literary value. Much of the credit for this belongs to Edward Stratemeyer who had perfected all the techniques of juvenile book production and to his daughter, Harriet Stratemeyer Adams, who was able to continue these policies and at the same time streamline and modernize the process.

# The Nancy Drew Books

A dealer at a flea market tried to inform me all about the Nancy Drew picture cover books I was looking at. "Nancy Drew was a man," she said. "What?" Her jaw got tighter and the cigarette hanging from her lips developed a longer ash as she repeated more sternly, "Nancy Drew was a man." The dealer did not know much more about this, but must have heard (as opposed to read) somewhere that the series was developed by a man (Stratemeyer). How could I burden this poor woman with more knowledge? She may have been just as startled as I was by her information if I told her that for me Nancy Drew was a woman who wore high heels while running through the woods clutching old clocks or crouching behind bushes at Red Gate Farm.

I always pictured Nancy Drew as she appeared on the dust jacket pictures when I read the books in the early 1950s. I enjoyed the Nancy Drew Mysteries because of the old-fashioned quality the 1930s to 1950s dust jacket pictures showed and was amazed in later years to see that the covers I liked so much had been updated. (I never cared for "modern" pictorial versions of the Bobbsey Twins, the Five Little Peppers or the Little Women either.)

The old dust jackets are what make Nancy Drew books the most valuable of all series books today. Now it is not uncommon for a dealer to ask at least $300.00 each for the first seven thick books with blank endpapers if they are in very good condition. Any white spine volume (1930 to 1945) brings high prices, especially for the earlier, thicker editions. Even the early picture covers now command respectable prices since they have some age (early 1960s) and there are many collectors who remember the books new in these formats.

There is a reason why there are still so many

Nancy Drew books in excellent condition from the World War II era around without dust jackets. In the early 1940s, huge piles of these books were sold in department stores, without dust jackets, for 25 cents each. They are remembered by Nancy Drew readers of the era as being for sale in such diverse locations as Detroit and Baltimore. It is highly likely that this phenomenon only lasted for a brief period. Perhaps it was an end-of-the-year clearance for one time only. At any rate, the books had to come from Grosset & Dunlap in their jacketless state for there to have been such large amounts of them remembered in different locations by different people.

In the **Ruth Fielding** chapter, it is reported how Stratemeyer developed many series books over a period of more than thirty years. His last girls' series, Nancy Drew, was the perfection of many different types of books for young people and all the elements that made juvenile mysteries exciting came together properly for this set. An enormous amount of credit must also go to Stratemeyer's daughter, Harriet Stratemeyer Adams (1892-1982), who protected the Nancy Drew image and led the public to believe that "Carolyn Keene" wrote the Nancy Drew books. In 1967, she "revealed" that her father had written the first three books and that she did the others. This was because of *My Father was Uncle Wiggley*, the biography of his father, Howard R. Garis (1873-1962), that Roger Garis published in 1966, in which many secrets of Stratemeyer Syndicate ghostwriters were reported. More "secrets" were divulged when Leslie McFarlane published his autobiography, *Ghost of the Hardy Boys*, in 1976 and, another ten years later, when Carol Billman's *Secret of the Stratemeyer Syndicate* was released. By the time of Mrs. Adams' death, it was known that the Nancy

Drew books had a different origin and development than she insisted, thinking that her big "secret" would protect and preserve the series better than the truth. (Even by 1967, "Carolyn Keene" was getting pretty old anyhow.)

In the many editions of *Farah's Guide*, David Farah gives a very detailed report on who wrote the outlines, who filled in the story and who edited each volume in the Nancy Drew Series. The most important plot outline creators are Edward Stratemeyer for Volumes 1 to 3 and Harriet Adams and her sister, Edna Stratemeyer Squier (1895-1974), for Volumes 4 to 56, which encompasses all of the "Classic Nancy Drew" books.

Mildred A. Wirt (Benson) wrote Volumes 1 to 7, 11 to 25 and 30. Walter Karig did Volumes 8 to 10; others did Volumes 26 to 29 and 32; and Mrs. Adams wrote Volumes 31 and 33 to 56. This means that Mildred A. Wirt Benson wrote twenty-three Nancy Drew books and Harriet Adams wrote twenty-five Nancy books, but Adams also created the plot outlines and edited most of the ones that she did not write.

The first twenty-six Nancy Drew dust jacket illustrations and internal black and white pictures were done by Russell H. Tandy with the exception of the dust jacket for Volume 11, *The Clue of the Broken Locket*, which was done by Ferdinand E. Warren, who did other series covers. The revised covers for Volumes 1 to 9 and 11 and the new covers for Volumes 27 to 29 were done by Bill Gillies, who was born in 1911. Gillies also did Hardy Boys and Ken Holt covers from 1948 to 1952. He did not do the frontispieces, reportedly because Grosset & Dunlap paid too little for them. Each girl on the Nancy Drew covers was Gillies' wife, Mary Agnes (born 1912). The most prolific dust jacket/picture cover artist for the Nancy Drew books was Rudy Nappi, born in 1923, who did sixty-four different covers. His work was one cover for Volumes 1 to 5; 8 to 9; 25 to 29; and 35 to 56 and he did two different covers for Volumes 10 to 24. The only Nancy Drew books that do not have Nappi covers are Volumes 6 and 7 (*The Secret of Red Gate Farm* and *The Clue in the Diary*).

It seems that the dust jacket and/or picture covers that are the most liked by collectors are the ones that they remember as youngsters. Those who remember the Tandy covers from the time they first read the books like them the best, and those who first saw Nancy Drew books with Nappi covers like them the best. Russell H. Tandy's Nancy Drew dust jackets always showed an action scene with an

Dust jacketed Nancy Drew by Editorial Bruguera, Spain, 1975. (*The Secret of the Old Clock*.)

attractive and contemporary Nancy. Her hair and her clothing were typical of the era, 1930 to 1940, a time period in which women's clothing and hairdos went through a huge change. The Gillies covers show a young woman of the early 1950s, but they are inconsistent in execution. Some covers, such as *The Mystery at the Ski Jump*, show an attractive Nancy in an exciting winter scene; others, such as *The Mystery at Lilac Inn*, depict a rather bug-eyed looking Nancy Drew eavesdropping on an uninteresting setting of three oddly dressed adults. The Rudy Nappi covers are the most varied and interesting from an artistic point of view. His early covers are a scene and are oftentimes just an updated copy of the Tandy art for the same cover. The last Nappi covers of the Classic Nancy Drew books usually show Nancy in close-up with objects around her reminiscent of the story of the book. These covers do not have the appearance of belonging to a specific time period although many of them are now more than thirty years old.

## Special Nancy Drew Classic Books

The most collectible and desirable, hence valuable, of all Nancy Drew books are the regular Grosset & Dunlap "Classic" books, Volumes 1 to 56 from 1930 to 1979. These are the ones that collectors desire the most. There are other Nancy Drew sets of books that were also available. The first group are the "Book Club Editions." See *Farah's Guide* for a more thorough breakdown of these books.

# Book Club Editions

**Type I.** These are called the "Cameo Editions" because there is a cameo design on the front cover. They were in the "Nancy Drew Reader's Club" in 1959. These taller-than-usual Grosset & Dunlap books had dust jackets, a color frontispiece and other illustrations by Polly Bolian. There were six books in 1959 and six more in 1960. None were given volume numbers on the books but they came from Volumes 30 to 35 in 1959 and Volumes 27 to 29; 36; and Volumes 1 to 2 in 1960.

**Type II.** In about 1962, the regular picture cover set was sold as a book club set with some changes: The title page has "Book Club Edition" printed on it; the back cover of the book is plain yellow; and there is no volume number printed on the spine. These books go up to at least Volume 33.

**Type III.** In about 1976, the first three Nancy Drew books were printed in a taller set. These books have plain yellow dust jackets with the third cover art (Nappi) centered on the front. On the inside flap they read "Book Club Edition." The hard covers are a plain mustard yellow.

**Type IV.** These books are from "The Nancy Drew Twin Thriller Book Club" from the mid 1970s. Each picture cover shows a picture by Rudy Nappi that is about two-thirds of the cover and is a combination scene of the two regular Nancy Drew mysteries combined in the book. There is a taller and a shorter set of these books. The eight taller titles are sets of the first sixteen books in pairs. The shorter set includes these and then begins with Volumes 18 to 19 as one book, Volumes 20 to 21 and Volumes 22 to 23. The next four books are Volumes 25 to 26 through Volumes 31 to 32. Then they pick up as Volumes 35 to 36 through Volumes 53 to 54. To finish off the set there is a Volumes 33 to 34 and Volumes 17 to 24, making a total of twenty-seven different books (fifty-four volumes of Nancy Drew mysteries).

# Special Editions

**Triple Edition.** A triple edition volume of the first three books in 1970. This is a picture cover book of 566 pages.

**AtlanticRichfield Offer.** In 1977, the Atlantic-Richfield [sic] Company offered fifty-four Hardy Boys books and fifty-four Nancy Drew books in a plan called "Hardy Boys - Nancy Drew Mystery Stories Series." The first two titles of each set were free in one box and the customer then received the rest of the books for $1.98 plus 35 cents postage and handling for each book. Either the Hardy Boys or Nancy Drew (or both) could be chosen. The books were sent at ninety-day intervals in two sets of seventeen books and one set of nineteen books, "charged automatically to your Arco credit card." The two first volumes were free to keep "unconditionally." The books were the regular picture cover books of the era and were not marked in any special way.

**Applewood.** In 1991, Applewood Books of Bedford, Massachusetts, began to publish "Facsimile Editions" of the original Nancy Drew Mystery Stories. These books are somewhat similar to the originals, but many shortcuts are taken with them: The binding with its narrow spine is not like the older books; the hard board covers are not like any that Grosset & Dunlap produced; the top page edges are not tinted; the endpapers are blank beyond the books that were first produced this way; the four internals are all bound into the book in the front, in reverse order; and the early books from Applewood had gold edges on the dust jackets and a huge gold seal on the front citing the fact that they are facsimile books. Other than this, they are rather nice. So far (early 2000) the first thirteen books are available. There is a similar set of Hardy Boys books from Applewood and the first two Judy Bolton books were done, but because they were not successful they have been discontinued.

**Smithmark.** In 1999, the first three Nancy Drew titles were bound together in one volume by Smithmark Publishers, a Division of U.S. Media Holdings, Inc., by arrangement with Pocket Books, a division of Simon & Schuster, Inc. This is a red hardback book with a dust jacket. The dust jacket uses the three latest pictures from the Grosset & Dunlap books. It is obvious that these pictures originated as very cheap color copies taken from the Grosset & Dunlap books instead of from any sort of original art. Other than this, the books are nicely produced and they sold for only $9.98. The inside flap on the Nancy Drew dust jacket mentions that the series has been "thrilling readers for more than 70 years...Since its inception by Carolyn M. Keene...in 1927." It must be difficult to include so many errors in so few words! The texts are the revised Grosset & Dunlap ones, but the pages are numbered consecutively up to page 558. A similar Hardy Boys book was also available. The binding is nice.

# Foreign Editions

There are also many foreign editions of the Nancy Drew books. In Great Britain, in the 1960s, Samson Low had a hardback series with Dana Girls "Flashlight" endpapers and dust jackets with different numbering than Grosset & Dunlap; in the 1970s, Armada published a paperback series also with different numbering; and, in the 1980s, Collins had a picture cover series with the same covers as Grosset & Dunlap but with the Armada numbering system. The Collins set began with *The Secret of Shadow Ranch* and had *The Thirteenth Pearl* as Volume 50. Many other countries, such as Iceland, Israel and Spain also published the series. An interesting feature of the Spanish edition of the 1970s from Editorial Bruguera, S.A. is that the illustrations are done in a comic strip format.

# Grosset & Dunlap

Grosset & Dunlap is the favorite publisher of everyone who collects series books. The company's products from the beginning of the 20th century until the early 1990s are the books that are the most collected and respected now. This is because of the nice presentation of the books, with their cheerful and colorful dust jackets and covers and the fact that the most popular series books came from this company.

Grosset & Dunlap began in 1898 when partners George Dunlap and Alex Grosset went into business in New York. At first the company published reprints for the adult market. The first successful juvenile series was Edward Stratemeyer's Tom Swift, which began in 1910. By 1950, Grosset & Dunlap was the leading publisher of juvenile books in the United States, but it began to decline in importance after that point and later became a part of Filmways, an entertainment company, and then G.P. Putnam's Sons Publishers.

In 1979, the Stratemeyer Syndicate switched from Grosset & Dunlap, with whom it had been associated for about seventy years, to Simon & Schuster. This meant that Grosset & Dunlap lost its important series books—The Hardy Boys, Nancy Drew and The Bobbsey Twins. In 1982, a court decision gave Grosset & Dunlap the rights to the Stratemeyer books that it had published up to 1979 and Simon & Schuster took over the three successful series and produced them as paperbacks with many titles in each set released per year. In 1984, Simon & Schuster purchased the Stratemeyer Syndicate.

As of this writing, there are still Grosset & Dunlap hardback picture cover books of the first fifty-eight Hardy Boys and the first fifty-six Nancy Drew titles. The Bobbsey Twins books were discontinued in about 1998 after having been in production for almost one-hundred years. It is probably just a matter of time before the Hardy Boys and Nancy Drew will end as a Grosset & Dunlap series also, as the same volumes with very little change in design have been marketed from 1987 until the present time. I have noticed for about two years that many of the chain bookstores that always stocked great quantities of the Grosset & Dunlap books no longer carry a wide selection of them.

# Nancy Drew Covers

| | 1st | 2nd | 3rd | 4th | Nancy Drew Covers |
|---|---|---|---|---|---|
| 1. | x | x | x | | *The Secret of the Old Clock* |
| 2. | x | x | x | | *The Hidden Staircase* |
| 3. | x | x | x | | *The Bungalow Mystery* |
| 4. | x | x | x | | *The Mystery at Lilac Inn* |
| 5. | x | x | x | | *The Secret at Shadow Ranch* |
| 6. | x | x | | | *The Secret of Red Gate Farm* |
| 7. | x | x | | | *The Clue in the Diary* |
| 8. | x | x | x | | *Nancy's Mysterious Letter* |
| 9. | x | x | x | | *The Sign of the Twisted Candles* |
| 10. | x | x | x | | *The Password to Larkspur Lane* |
| 11. | x | x | x | x | *The Clue of the Broken Locket* |
| 12. | x | x | x | | *The Message in the Hollow Oak* |
| 13. | x | x | x | | *The Mystery of the Ivory Charm* |
| 14. | x | x | x | | *The Whispering Statue* |
| 15. | x | x | x | | *The Haunted Bridge* |
| 16. | x | x | x | | *The Clue of the Tapping Heels* |
| 17. | x | x | x | | *The Mystery of the Brass Bound Trunk* |
| 18. | x | x | x | | *The Mystery at the Moss-Covered Mansion* |
| 19. | x | x | x | | *The Quest of the Missing Map* |
| 20. | x | x | x | | *The Clue in the Jewel Box* |
| 21. | x | x | x | | *The Secret in the Old Attic* |
| 22. | x | x | x | | *The Clue in the Crumbling Wall* |

| | 1st | 2nd | 3rd | 4th | Nancy Drew Covers |
|---|---|---|---|---|---|
| 23. | x | x | x | | *The Mystery of the Tolling Bell* |
| 24. | x | x | x | | *The Clue in the Old Album* |
| 25. | x | x | | | *The Ghost of Blackwood Hall* |
| 26. | x | x | | | *The Clue of the Leaning Chimney* |
| 27. | x | x | | | *The Secret of the Wooden Lady* |
| 28. | x | x | | | *The Clue of the Black Keys* |
| 29. | x | x | | | *The Mystery at the Ski Jump* |
| 30. | x | x | | | *The Clue of the Velvet Mask* |
| 31. | x | x | | | *The Ringmaster's Secret* |
| 32. | x | x | | | *The Scarlet Slipper Mystery* |
| 33. | x | x | | | *The Witch Tree Symbol* |
| 34. | x | x | | | *The Hidden Window Mystery* |
| 35. | x | | | | *The Haunted Showboat* |
| 36. | x | | | | *The Secret of the Golden Pavilion* |
| 37. | x | | | | *The Clue in the Old Stagecoach* |
| 38. | x | | | | *The Mystery of the Fire Dragon* |
| 39. | x | | | | *The Clue of the Dancing Puppet* |
| 40. | x | | | | *The Moonstone Castle Mystery* |
| 41. | x | | | | *The Clue of the Whistling Bagpipes* |
| 42. | x | | | | *The Phantom of Pine Hill* |
| 43. | x | | | | *The Mystery of the 99 Steps* |
| 44. | x | | | | *The Clue in the Crossword Cipher* |
| 45. | x | | | | *The Spider Sapphire Mystery* |
| 46. | x | | | | *The Invisible Intruder* |
| 47. | x | | | | *The Mysterious Mannequin* |
| 48. | x | | | | *The Crooked Banister* |
| 49. | x | | | | *The Secret at Mirror Bay* |
| 50. | x | | | | *The Double Jinx Mystery* |
| 51. | x | | | | *The Mystery of the Glowing Eye* |
| 52. | x | | | | *The Secret of the Forgotten City* |
| 53. | x | | | | *The Sky Phantom* |
| 54. | x | | | | *The Strange Message in the Parchment* |
| 55. | x | | | | *Mystery of Crocodile Island* |
| 56. | x | | | | *The Thirteenth Pearl* |

# Nancy Drew Book Formats

## Grosset & Dunlap

I.  1930 - 1931
#1 - #7, including first editions #1 - #7
Thick light blue cloth cover with orange printing on front, dark blue printing on spine
Blank eps
Glossy frontis
Three glossy internals
White spine dj
Good paper

II. 1932 - 1943
#1 - #20, including first editions #8 - #20
Thick blue cover with orange printing and silhouette of Nancy (cloth in earlier years)
Orange silhouette eps
#1 to #13 have glossy frontis
Three glossy internals
#14 to #17 glossy frontis only
#17 through #20 frontis on plain paper; white spine dj; symbol of Nancy on spine begins in 1941
#19 has good or poor paper
#20 has poor paper

III. 1944 - 1946
   #1 - #23, including first editions #21 - #23
   Semi-thick blue cover with orange printing
      and silhouette
   Cloth covers have been replaced with
      imitation materials
   Orange silhouette endpapers
   Frontis on plain paper
   White spine dj w/spine symbol
   Wrap spine begins with #23
   Poor paper
*Variations:* the covers are various shades of blue,
have several types of finishes and are of poorer
quality.

IV. 1946
   #1 - #23
   Medium blue cover with dark blue printing
      and silhouette
   Orange silhouette eps
   Frontis on plain paper
   #1 - #22 white spine dj w/symbol
   #23 wrap spine dj
   Poor paper

V. 1947 - 1952
   #1 - #30, including first editions #24 - #30
   Medium blue cover with dark blue printing
      and silhouette
   Blue tweed cover begins ca. 1952
   1940s silhouette begins on front covers
   Mostly blue silhouette eps
   Frontis on plain paper
   (Reprints have spine symbol or wrap spine djs)
   1947 - early 1948 poor paper; after late 1948
      good paper
*Variations:* Some books have orange silhouette eps;
some have maroon Dana Girls eps.

VI. 1953 - 1958
   #1 - #35, including first editions #31 - #35
   Blue tweed cover with dark blue printing and
      silhouette
   Blue "Digger" eps (Nancy watches man digging)
   #1 - #31 frontis on plain paper
   #32 - #35 have frontis and five internals on
      plain paper
   (Reprints have spine symbol or wrap spine djs)
   Good paper

VII. 1959 - 1961
   #1 - #38, including first editions #36 - #38
   Blue tweed cover with dark blue printing and
      silhouette
   Blue Multi-Scene eps (22 scenes based on dust
      jackets)
   Frontis on plain paper; #32 - #38, revised texts
      of #1 - #4 and #6 have frontis and five
         internals on plain paper
      (Reprints have spine symbol djs or wrap djs)
   Good paper

VIII. 1962 - 1968
   #1 - #45, including first editions #39 - #45
   Yellow spine picture cover
   On back cover picture of Nancy behind tree
   Blue Multi-Scene eps, #1 - #6 and #8 - #38
   White Multi-Scene I eps (blue multi-scenes
      redrawn in ink), #39 - #45, revised texts
      #5, #7 - #11, and #25 - #29
   White Multi-Scene II eps (fifteen black and
      white drawings from djs and cover
      pictures) on some volumes
   Frontis on plain paper, #5 and #8 - #31
   Frontis and five internals on plain paper,
      #32 - #45 and revised texts #1 - #11
      and #25 - #29
   Good paper
*Variations:* Spines are various shades of yellow and
some fade easily, turning almost white.

IX. 1969-1981
   #1 - #56, including first editions #46 - #56
   Yellow spine picture cover. On back cover,
      picture of Nancy with magnifying glass
   Blue Multi-Scene endpapers #12 - #15,
      #17 - #18, #20 - #24 and #31 - #34
   White Multi-Scene II eps #35 - #56 and
      revised texts of #1 - #34
   Frontis on plain paper, #12 - #15,
      #17 - #18, #20 - #24, and #31
   Frontis and five internals on plain paper,
      #32 - #56 and revised texts #1 - #34
   Good paper
*Variations:* Some volumes have White Multi-Scene I
eps

X. 1982 - 1986
   #1 - #56
   Yellow spine picture cover. On back cover,
      picture of Nancy with magnifying glass
   Double Oval eps (two crude portraits of
      Nancy in ink)
   Frontis and five internals on plain paper,
      #35 - #56 and revised texts of #1 - #34
   Good paper

Note: Since 1987 the picture covers have been on
smooth, shiny stock.

# 1. The Secret of the Old Clock

1930 Edition. 210 Pages.

Sixteen-year-old Nancy Drew searches for Josiah Crowley's will to prevent the Topham family from inheriting an estate they do not deserve.

**1**. DJ A.

1959 Edition. 180 Pages.

The revision is a condensed and modernized version of the same mystery. Nancy meets the poor and deserving Turners at the beginning of this book instead of encountering the disagreeable Topham sisters first. Many chapters have new titles.

Dust Jacket A. - 1930 - 1950
Illustrator: Russell H. Tandy
| | |
|---|---|
| Format I. | $25.00-$300.00+ |
| Format II. | $15.00-$250.00 |
| Format III. | $8.00-$100.00 |
| Format IV. | $10.00-$125.00 |
| Format V. | $5.00-$50.00 |

Dust Jacket B. - 1950 - 1961
Illustrator: Bill Gillies
| | |
|---|---|
| Format V. | $5.00-$50.00 |
| Format VI. | $5.00-$45.00 |
| Format VII. | $5.00-$40.00 |

Picture Cover A. - 1962 - 1966
(Same as Dust Jacket B)
| | |
|---|---|
| Format VIII. | $4.00-$20.00 |

Picture Cover B. - 1966+
Illustrator: Rudy Nappi
| | |
|---|---|
| Format VIII. | $4.00-$20.00 |
| Format IX. | $3.00-$15.00 |
| Format X. | $3.00-$10.00 |

Note: Dust Jacket B is on both versions of *The Secret of the Old Clock*.

**1**. DJ B/PC A.

**1**. PC B.

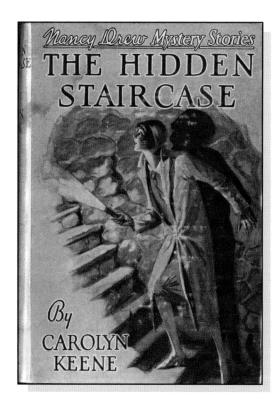

**2.** DJ A.

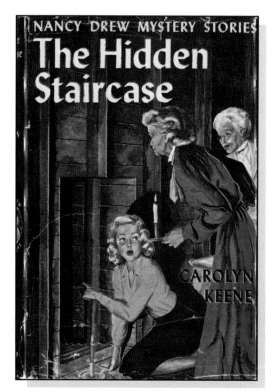

**2.** DJ B/PC A.

## 2. The Hidden Staircase

1930 Edition. 206 Pages.

Rosemary and Floretta Trumbull, friends of Abigail Rowen from *The Secret of the Old Clock*, are having problems with ghosts in their home. Nancy finds a secret door leading to a secret staircase and encounters danger.

1959 Edition. 182 Pages.

This plot still involves a haunted house, but the elderly sisters are now relatives of Nancy's friend, Helen. This is not just a revision; it is a new story, as all the details are changed. All twenty chapters have different titles than in the twenty-five-chapter book.

Dust Jacket A. - 1930 - 1950
Illustrator: Russell H. Tandy
Format I.        $25.00-$300.00+
Format II.       $15.00-$250.000
Format III.      $8.00-$100.00
Format IV.      $10.00-$125.00
Format V.       $5.00-$50.00

Dust Jacket B. - 1950 - 1951
Illustrator: Bill Gillies
Format V.       $5.00-$50.00
Format VI.      $5.00-$45.00
Format VII.     $5.00-$40.00

Picture Cover A. - 1962 - 1965
(Same as Dust Jacket B)
Format VIII.    $4.00-$20.00

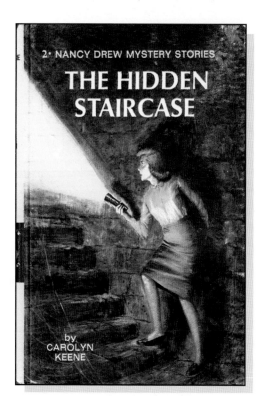

**2.** PC B.

Picture Cover B. - 1966+
Illustrator: Rudy Nappi
Format VIII.    $4.00-$20.00
Format IX.      $3.00-$15.00
Format X.       $3.00-$10.00

Note: Dust Jacket B is on both versions of *The Hidden Staircase*.

# 3. The Bungalow Mystery

1930 Edition. 204 Pages.

A stranger, Laura Pendleton, saves Nancy and Helen from drowning when their boat is overturned in a storm. Nancy later helps to free Laura from a cruel guardian.

Note: This is the third Tandy dust jacket in a row in which Nancy wears the same blue outfit.

1960 Edition. 180 Pages.

The story is condensed and updated with new chapter titles.

Dust Jacket A. - 1930 - 1950
Illustrator: Russell H. Tandy
| | |
|---|---|
| Format I. | $25.00-$300.00+ |
| Format II. | $15.00-$250.00 |
| Format III. | $8.00-$100.00 |
| Format IV. | $10.00-$125.00 |
| Format V. | $5.00-$50.00 |

Dust Jacket B. - 1950 - 1961
Illustrator: Bill Gillies
| | |
|---|---|
| Format V. | $5.00-$50.00 |
| Format VI. | $5.00-$45.00 |
| Format VII. | $5.00-$40.00 |
| 1960 (Second Text) Edition | $55.00 |

Picture Cover A. - 1962 - 1966
(Same as Dust Jacket B)
| | |
|---|---|
| Format VIII. | $4.00-$20.00 |

Picture Cover B. - 1967+
Illustrator: Rudy Nappi
| | |
|---|---|
| Format VIII. | $4.00-$20.00 |
| Format X. | $3.00-$10.00 |

Note: Dust Jacket B is on both versions of *The Bungalow Mystery*.

**3**. DJ A.

**3**. DJ B/PC A.

**3**. PC B.

# 4. The Mystery at Lilac Inn

1930 Edition. 200 Pages.

When Nancy stopped her blue roadster (which matched the color of her frock) at Lilac Inn, she encountered her friend, Emily Crandall. Later Nancy helped Emily regain her stolen diamonds, valued at "not a cent less than forty thousand dollars."

Note: Tandy shows Nancy in a slightly different outfit than on the dust jackets of the first three books, but her costume is the same color.

1961 Edition. 180 Pages.

In a new story with the same title, Nancy and Helen go to Lilac Inn because their canoe capsized nearby. Nancy helps her friend, Emily Willoughby, the owner of the inn, recover stolen diamonds and expose an actress who had been impersonating Nancy.

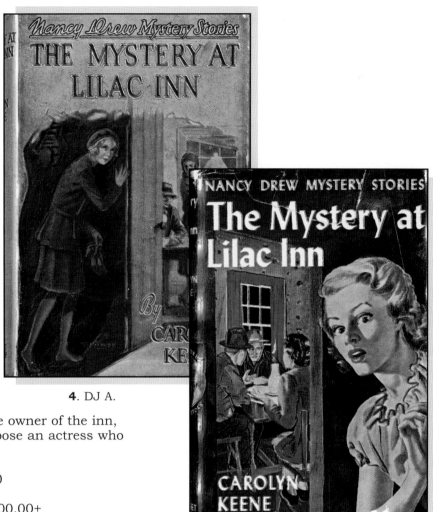

**4**. DJ A.

Dust Jacket A. - 1930 - 1950
Illustrator: Russell H. Tandy
| Format I. | $30.00-$300.00+ |
|---|---|
| Format II. | $15.00-$250.00 |
| Format III. | $8.00-$100.00 |
| Format IV. | $8.00-$100.00 |
| Format V. | $5.00-$50.00 |

Dust Jacket B. - 1950 - 1961
Illustrator: Bill Gillies
| Format V. | $5.00-$50.000 |
|---|---|
| Format VI. | $5.00-$45.00 |
| Format VII. | $5.00-$40.00 |

Dust Jacket C. - 1961
Illustrator: Rudy Nappi
| Format VII. | $5.00-$75.00 |
|---|---|

Picture Cover A. - 1962+
(Same as Dust Jacket C)
| Format VIII. | $4.00-$20.00 |
|---|---|
| Format IX. | $3.00-$15.00 |
| Format X. | $3.00-$10.00 |

Note: *The Mystery at Lilac Inn* is the only Nancy Drew book that has three different dust jackets.

**4**. DJ B.

**4**. DJ C/PC A.

# 5. The Secret at Shadow Ranch

1931 Edition. 203 Pages.

Cousins Elizabeth (Bess) Marvin and George Fayne join Nancy for a vacation in "the West." They restore Alice Regnor's father to the family and solve other problems.

1965 Edition. **The Secret of Shadow Ranch**. 175 Pages.

The re-write has a slightly different title and a much different plot: The girls go to Arizona and solve the mystery of a ghost horse and a hidden treasure even though a cryptic note had warned them to stay away from Shadow Ranch.

Dust Jacket A. - 1931 - 1950
Illustrator: Russell H. Tandy
| | |
|---|---|
| Format I. | $40.00-$275.00 |
| Format II. | $15.00-$235.00 |
| Format III. | $8.00-$100.00 |
| Format IV. | $10.00-$125.00 |
| Format V. | $5.00-$50.00 |

Dust Jacket B. - 1950 - 1961
Illustrator: Bill Gillies
| | |
|---|---|
| Format V. | $5.00-$50.00 |
| Format VI. | $5.00-$45.00 |
| Format VII. | $5.00-$45.00 |

Picture Cover A. - 1962 - 1966
(Same as Dust Jacket B)
| | |
|---|---|
| Format VIII. | $4.00-$20.00 |

Picture Cover B. - 1966+
Illustrator: Rudy Nappi
| | |
|---|---|
| Format VIII. | $4.00-$20.00 |
| Format IX. | $3.00-$15.00 |
| Format X. | $3.00-$10.00 |

Note: The second edition and second title is only in Picture Cover B.

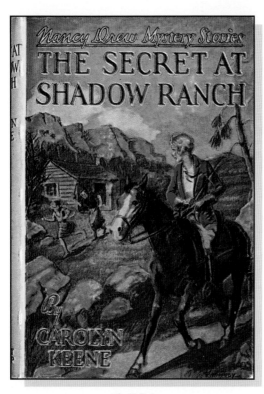

**5**. DJ A.

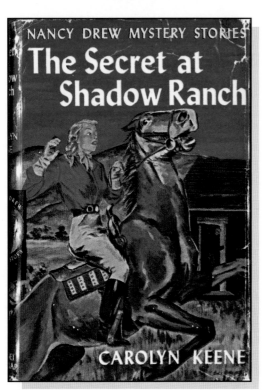

**5**. DJ B/PC A.

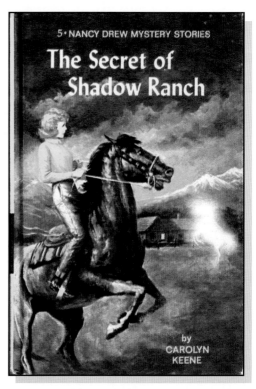

**5**. PC B.

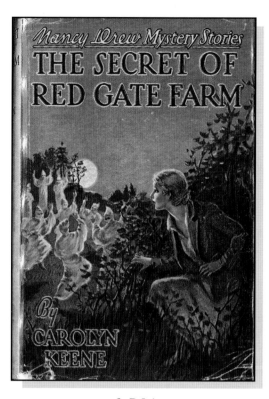

**6**. DJ A.

**6**. DJ B/PC A.

# 6. The Secret of Red Gate Farm

1931 Edition. 208 Pages.

Nancy helps Millie Burd get to her grandmother's
farm when she is not able to find employment. At
Red Gate Farm, they encounter a strange sect that
performs odd ceremonies at night while dressed in
white robes and that may be involved in a counter-
feit money ring.

1961 Edition. 178 Pages.

The revision is a shorter version with minor updated elements.

Dust Jacket A. - 1931 - 1950
Illustrator: Russell H. Tandy
Format I.        $40.00-$275.00
Format II.       $5.00-$235.00
Format III.      $8.00-$100.00
Format IV.       $10.00-$125.00
Format V.        $5.00-$50.00

Dust Jacket B. - 1950 - 1961
Illustrator: Bill Gillies
Format V.        $5.00-$50.00
Format VI.       $5.00-$45.00
Format VII.      $5.00-$40.00
    1961 Edition   $60.00

Picture Cover A. - 1962+
(Same as Dust Jacket B)
Format VIII.     $4.00-$20.00
Format IX.       $3.00-$15.00
Format X.        $3.00-$10.00

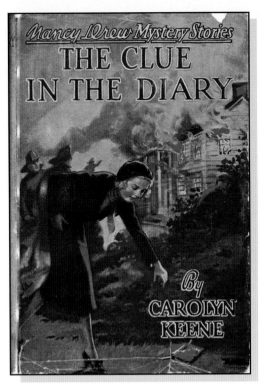

**7**. DJ A.

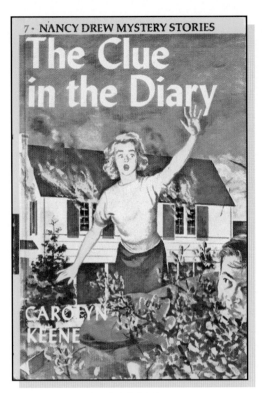

**7**. DJ B/PC A.

# 7. The Clue in the Diary

1932 Edition. 202 Pages.

A mysterious stranger drops a book when he is running away from a burning house. The book is a diary containing a clue that restores substantial funds to people who have been swindled, particularly the Swenson family.

1962 Edition. 174 Pages.

The original book is condensed and modernized.

Dust Jacket A. - 1932 - 1950
Illustrator: Russell H. Tandy

| | |
|---|---|
| Format I. | $100.00-$500.00 |
| Format II. | $15.00-$250.00 |
| Format III. | $8.00-$100.00 |
| Format IV. | $10.00-$125.00 |
| Format V. | $5.00-$50.00 |

Dust Jacket B. - 1950 - 1961
Illustrator: Bill Gillies

| | |
|---|---|
| Format V. | $5.00-$50.00 |
| Format VI. | $5.00-$45.00 |
| Format VII. | $5.00-$50.00 |

Picture Cover A. - 1962+
(Same as Dust Jacket B)

| | |
|---|---|
| Format VIII. | $4.00-$20.00 |
| Original Text (1962) | $40.00 |
| Format IX. | $3.00-$15.00 |
| Format X. | $3.00-$10.00 |

Note: There was only one printing of Format I (Blank Endpapers, printed in 1931) and Format VIII (Picture Cover with original text).

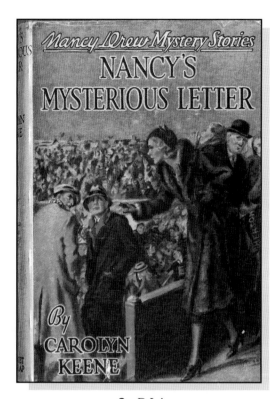

**8**. DJ A.

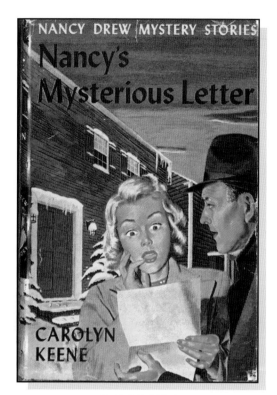

**8**. DJ B/PC A.

# 8.    Nancy's Mysterious Letter

1932 Edition. 209 Pages.

Right after Mr. Dixon, "the letter man," delivers an envelope from England to Nancy, his mail pouch is stolen. The letter that Nancy received was meant for another Miss Drew and was about an inheritance. Nancy searches for the real heiress and also solves the mystery of the stolen mail.

1968 Edition. 174 Pages.

In this shortened, modernized edition mailman Ira Dixon is "elderly Ira Nixon."

    Dust Jacket A. - 1932 - 1950
    Illustrator: Russell H. Tandy
    Format II.          $12.00-$250.00
    Format III.         $8.00-$185.00
    Format IV.          $8.00-$125.00
    Format V.           $5.00-$50.00

    Dust Jacket B. - 1950 - 1961
    Illustrator: Bill Gillies
    Format V.           $5.00-$50.00
    Format VI.          $5.00-$45.00
    Format VII.         $5.00-$40.00

    Picture Cover A. - 1962 - 1967
    (Same as Dust Jacket B)
    Format VIII.        $4.00-$20.00

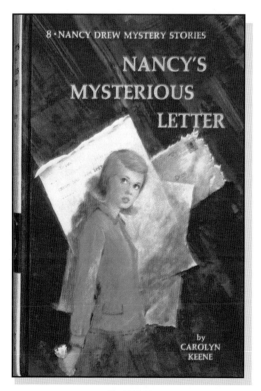

**8**. PC B.

Picture Cover B. - 1968+
Illustrator: Rudy Nappi
Format VIII.        $5.00-$20.00
Format IX.          $3.00-$15.00
Format X.           $3.00-$10.00

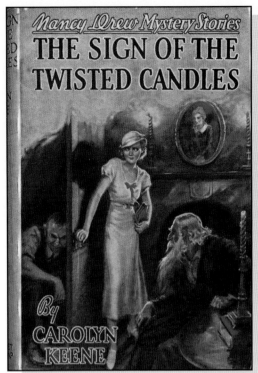

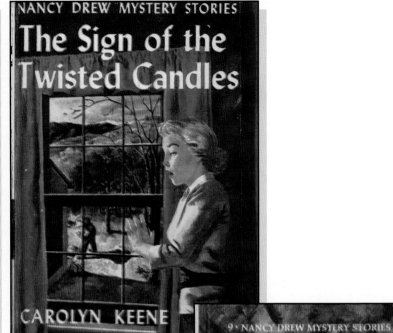

**9.** DJ A.

**9.** DJ B/PC A.

## 9. The Sign of the Twisted Candles

1933 Edition. 217 Pages.

Nancy, George and Bess encounter another mystery at an old inn. At The Sign of the Twisted Candles, Nancy meets the owner, one-hundred-year-old Asa Sidney, whose wealth came from his twisted candle invention. Nancy also befriends poor Sadie Wipple who is abused by her foster parents. Nancy solves mysteries connected with Sadie's birth and Asa Sidney's will.

1968 Edition. 176 Pages.

In the updated and revised edition of the book, Sadie's name is modernized as Carol.

**9.** PC B.

Dust Jacket A. - 1932 - 1950
Illustrator: Russell H. Tandy
Format II.          $12.00-$250.00
Format III.         $8.00-$185.00
Format IV.          $8.00-$125.00
Format V.           $5.00-$50.00

Dust Jacket B. - 1950 - 1961
Illustrator: Bill Gillies
Format V.           $5.00-$50.00
Format VI.          $5.00-$45.00
Format VII.         $5.00-$40.00

Picture Cover A. - 1962 - 1967
(Same as Dust Jacket B)
Format VIII.        $4.00-$25.00

Picture Cover B. - 1968+
Illustrator: Rudy Nappi
Format VIII.        $5.00-$20.00
Format IX.          $3.00-$15.00
Format X.           $3.00-$10.00

Note: Three different artists' interpretation of Nancy Drew is most apparent on the three cover designs for *The Sign of the Twisted Candles*. On the 1930s cover, Nancy looks like Hollywood movie stars of the era and much too old to be a teenage detective. On the second cover, Nancy does look like girls her age did in 1950. The third cover is a good portrait of how a girl Nancy's age may have looked in the late 1960s.

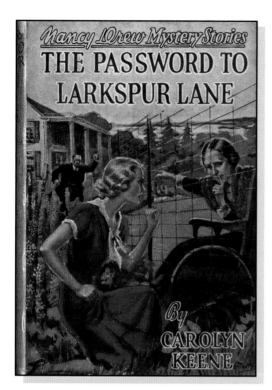

**10**. DJ A.

**10**. PC A.

## 10. The Password to Larkspur Lane

1933 Edition. 220 Pages.

A carrier pigeon lands at Nancy's feet while she is cutting larkspurs in her garden. The message the bird is carrying leads Nancy to another location planted with larkspurs. This is a rest home where elderly women are held against their will and swindled of their fortunes. Nancy is particularly interested in Mrs. Eldridge, whom she saves with the help of her friend, Helen Corning.

1966 Edition. **Password to Larkspur Lane**. 175 Pages.

The updated version has a slightly different title and some plot elements are changed. Nancy's friend, Helen (Archer), is now the granddaughter of the Cornings.

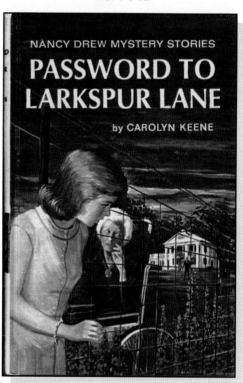

**10**. PC B.

Dust Jacket A. - 1933 - 1961
Illustrator: Russell H. Tandy
Rare 1932 printings        $  ?
Format II.        $12.00-$250.00
Format III.        $8.00-$185.00
Format IV.        $8.00-$125.00
Format V.        $5.00-$50.00
Format VI.        $5.00-$45.00
Format VII.        $5.00-$40.00

Picture Cover A. - 1962 - 1965
Illustrator: Rudy Nappi
Format VIII.        $5.00-$25.00

Picture Cover B. - 1966+
Illustrator: Rudy Nappi
Format IX.        $3.00-$15.00
Format X.        $3.00-$10.00

Note: The originals of *The Password to Larkspur Lane*, *The Haunted Bridge* and *The Mystery of the Brass Bound Trunk* are the longest Nancy Drew Mystery Stories at 220 pages each.

# 11. The Clue of the Broken Locket

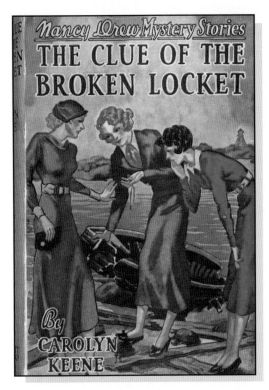

**11**. DJ A.

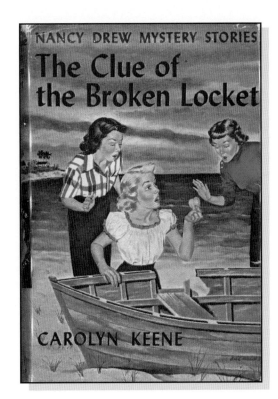

**11**. DJ B.

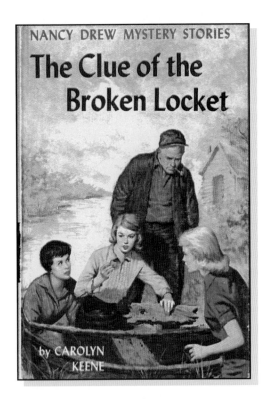

**11**. PC A.

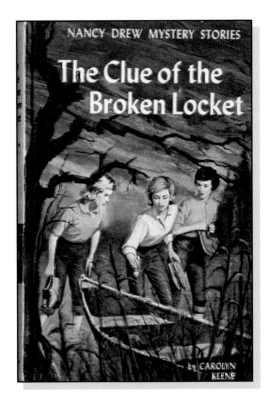

**11**. PC B.

## 11. The Clue of the Broken Locket

1934 Edition. 219 Pages.

A broken locket provides the important clue in leading Nancy to the real parents of the twins who were adopted by pushy singer Kitty Blair and her dominated husband Johnny.

1965 Edition. 178 Pages.

The update on this title is a new story. Nancy, George and Bess visit Pudding Stone Lodge on Misty Lake and solve two mysteries. One has to do with a singer whose record company is cheating her. The other is about a treasure that was hidden before the Civil War.

> Dust Jacket A. - 1934 - 1950
> Illustrator: Ferdinand E. Warren
> Format II.          $12.00-$250.00
> Format III.         $8.00-$185.00
> Format IV.          $8.00-$125.00
> Format V.           $5.00-$50.00
>
> Dust Jacket B. - 1950 - 1961
> Illustrator: Bill Gillies
> Format V.           $5.00-$50.00
> Format VI.          $5.00-$45.00
> Format VII.         $5.00-$40.00
>
> Picture Cover A. - 1962 - 1965
> Illustrator: Rudy Nappi
> Format VIII.        $6.00-$25.00
>     1965 Edition   $40.00
>
> Picture Cover B. - 1965+
> Illustrator: Rudy Nappi
> Format VIII.        $5.00-$20.00
> Format IX.          $3.00-$15.00
> Format X.           $3.00-$10.00

Note: The man standing behind Nancy on the third cover is a self-portrait of artist Rudy Nappi. *The Clue of the Broken Locket* is the only Nancy Drew title from Grosset & Dunlap to have four different cover pictures.

## 12. The Message in the Hollow Oak

1935 Edition. 218 Pages.

Nancy won some land in Canada by suggesting a title for a mystery story on a radio program. Problems develop when it is believed that there is gold on Nancy's property.

1972 Edition. 182 pages, including the "Postscript."

The new mystery with the same title, *The Message in the Hollow Oak,* is about a message hidden in a hollow tree in Illinois centuries earlier. While searching for the tree, Nancy and her friends encounter archeologists who are excavating a Hopewell Indian mound and fortune hunters intent on mischief.

> Dust Jacket A. - 1935 - 1961
> Illustrator: Russell H. Tandy
> Format II.          $12.00-$250.00
> Format III.         $8.00-$185.00
> Format IV.          $8.00-$125.00
> Format V.           $5.00-$50.00
>   W/Dana eps*       $7.00-$70.00
> Format VI.          $5.00-$45.00
> Format VII.         $5.00-$40.00
>
> Dust Jacket B. - 1961
> Illustrator: Rudy Nappi
> Format VII.         $5.00-$80.00+
>
> Picture Cover A. - 1962 - 1972
> (Same as Dust Jacket B)
> Format VIII.        $5.00-$20.00
> Format IX.          $3.00-$15.00
>
> Picture Cover B. - 1972+
> Illustrator: Rudy Nappi
> Format IX.          $3.00-$15.00
> Format X.           $3.00-$10.00

Note: Compare Dust Jackets A and B. It is the exact same scene by two different artists but each uses styles and trends of his own era. This practice of using the same scene for an updated cover continues through Volume 27.

*The endpapers are the ones used in the Dana Girls books of the time and show two girls reading a letter. The printing is in maroon and white.

## 12. The Message in the Hollow Oak

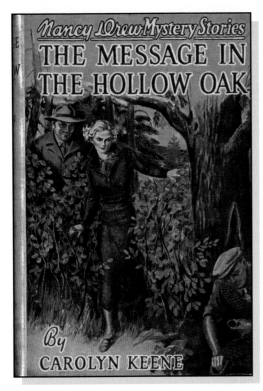

**12**. DJ A.

**12**. DJ B/PC A.

**12**. PC B.

**13**. DJ A.

**13**. PC A.

## 13. The Mystery of the Ivory Charm

1936 Edition. 216 Pages.

When Nancy and her friends watch a circus unloading from a train they become acquainted with the boy Coya who is mistreated by his father. Nancy discovers that Rai, who gave her a beautiful elephant charm, is not the real father of Coya. What is the secret of this Ivory Charm?

1974 Edition. 179 Pages.

In the updated abridgment of the tale, Coya's name is changed to Rishi and other details are changed as well.

Dust Jacket A. - 1936 - 1961
Illustrator: Russell H. Tandy
Format II.         $12.00-$250.00
Format III.       $8.00-$185.00
Format IV.       $8.00-$125.00
Format V.        $5.00-$50.00
Format VI.       $5.00-$45.00
Format VII.      $5.00-$40.00

Picture Cover A. - 1962 - 1973
Illustrator: Rudy Nappi
Format VIII.     $5.00-$20.00
Format IX.       $3.00-$15.00

Picture Cover B. - 1974+
Illustrator: Rudy Nappi
Format IX.       $3.00-$15.00
Format X.        $3.00-$10.00

**13**. PC B.

## 14. The Whispering Statue

1937 Edition. 217 Pages.

Nancy travels to Old Estate at Sea Cliff to see a marble statue that she is told resembles her. She solves a mystery while there, aided by the little dog, Togo, whom she met at the beginning of the story and adopts at the end.

1970 Edition. 179 Pages.

In the new book of the same title, Nancy once again solves two mysteries. The first concerns the disposition of a collection of rare books in which a swindle may be involved and the second is about the theft of a beautiful marble statue from the lawn of a yacht club.

Dust Jacket A. - 1937 - 1961
Illustrator: Russell H. Tandy
| | |
|---|---|
| Format II. | $12.00-$250.00 |
| Format III. | $8.00-$185.00 |
| Format IV. | $8.00-$125.00 |
| Format V. | $5.00-$50.00 |
| W/Dana eps* | $7.00-$70.00 |
| Format VI. | $5.00-$45.00 |
| Format VII. | $5.00-$40.00 |

Picture Cover A. - 1962 - 1970
Illustrator: Rudy Nappi
| | |
|---|---|
| Format VIII. | $5.00-$20.00 |
| Format IX. | $3.00-$15.00 |

Picture Cover B. - 1970+
Illustrator: Rudy Nappi
| | |
|---|---|
| Format IX. | $3.00-$15.00 |
| Format X. | $3.00-$10.00 |

*The endpapers are the ones used in the Dana Girls books of the time and show two girls reading a letter. The printing is in maroon and white.

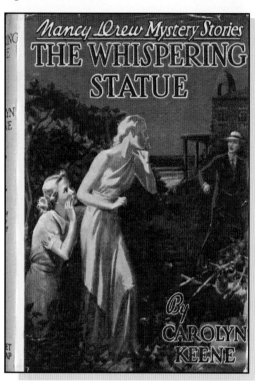

**14**. DJ A.

**14**. PC A.

**14**. PC B.

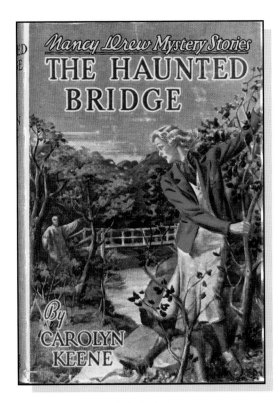

**15**. DJ A.

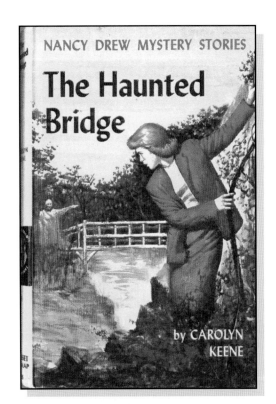

**15**. PC A.

## 15. The Haunted Bridge

1937 Edition. 220 Pages.

Nancy, Bess and George go to Deer Mountain Hotel as guests of Nancy's father, Attorney Carson Drew, to relax. Nancy plays in a golf tournament, helps her father apprehend a gang of jewel thieves and discovers the mystery behind the ghost on the grounds of the hotel.

1972 Edition. 180 Pages.

The book is abridged and updated and Nancy still solves two mysteries and wins the golf tournament.

**15**. PC B.

Dust Jacket A. - 1937 - 1961
Illustrator: Russell H. Tandy
Format II.          $12.00-$250.00
Format III.         $8.00-$185.00
Format IV.          $8.00-$125.00
Format V.           $5.00-$50.00
Format VI.          $5.00-$45.00
Format VII.         $5.00-$40.00

Picture Cover A. - 1962 - 1971
Illustrator: Rudy Nappi
Format VIII.        $5.00-$20.00
Format IX.          $3.00-$15.00

Picture Cover B. - 1972+
Illustrator: Rudy Nappi
Format IX.          $3.00-$15.00
Format X.           $3.00-$10.00

# 16. The Clue of the Tapping Heels

**16**. DJ A.

1939 Edition. 214 Pages.

Nancy, who is an accomplished tap dancer, helps cat fancier and actress Miss Carter with the theft of her cats and the administration of a will by sending Morse code signals with her feet while tied up.

1969 Edition. 176 Pages.

In the abridged and modernized version of the book, Nancy reunites Miss Carter with her lost love, as she did in the first edition.

Dust Jacket A. - 1939 - 1961
Illustrator: Russell H. Tandy
Format II.          $12.00-$250.00
Format III.         $8.00-$185.00
Format IV.          $8.00-$125.00
Format V.           $5.00-$50.00
Format VI.          $5.00-$45.00
Format VII.         $5.00-$40.00

Picture Cover A. - 1962 - 1968
Illustrator: Rudy Nappi
Format VIII.        $5.00-$20.00
Format IX.          $3.00-$15.00

Picture Cover B. - 1969+
Illustrator: Rudy Nappi
Format IX.          $3.00-$15.00
Format X.           $3.00-$10.00

**16**. PC A.

**16**. PC B.

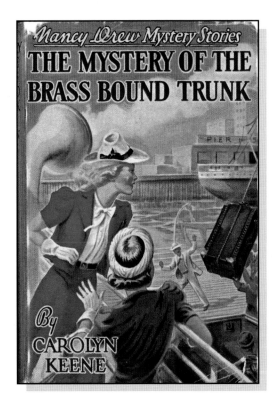
**17**. DJ A.

**17**. PC A.

## 17. The Mystery of the Brass Bound Trunk

1940 Edition. 220 Pages.

Nancy, Bess and George travel to South America by sea and bring a ring of jewel smugglers to justice. (This book was published during World War II!)

1976 Edition. **Mystery of the Brass-Bound Trunk**. 180 Pages.

This is a new title for a brand new story. Nancy and her friends share a cabin on a ship sailing from Rotterdam in the Netherlands to New York with South African Nelda Detweiler. Nelda is accused of stealing a diamond bracelet and Nancy locates the real thieves before the ship docks in New York.

Dust Jacket A. - 1940 - 1961
Illustrator: Russell H. Tandy
Format II.      $12.00-$250.00
Format III.     $8.00-$185.00
Format IV.     $8.00-$125.00
Format V.      $5.00-$50.00
Format VI.     $5.00-$45.00
Format VII.    $5.00-$15.00

Picture Cover A. - 1962 - 1976
Illustrator: Rudy Nappi
Format VIII.   $5.00-$20.00
Format IX.     $3.00-$15.00

**17**. PC B.

Picture Cover B. - 1976+
Illustrator: Rudy Nappi
Format IX.     $3.00-$15.00
Format X.      $3.00-$10.00

# 18. The Mystery at the Moss-Covered Mansion

**18**. DJ A.

1941 Edition. 215 Pages.

Nancy and her friends, with help from Carson Drew, investigate strange doings at a mysterious mansion and recover a lost fortune in cash.

1971 Edition. **Mystery of the Moss-Covered Mansion**. 177 Pages.

The short version of the variance of the title is a new story. In this mystery, Carson Drew's friend, Mr. Billington, is charged with sending explosives into the Kennedy Space Center. During the investigation Nancy discovers strange happenings at a spooky old Florida mansion.

Dust Jacket A. - 1941 - 1961
Illustrator: Russell H. Tandy
Format II.          $12.00-$250.00
Format III.         $8.00-$185.00
Format IV.          $8.00-$125.00
Format V.           $5.00-$50.00
Format VI.          $5.00-$45.00
Format VII.         $5.00-$40.00

Picture Cover A. - 1962 - 1971
Illustrator: Rudy Nappi
Format VIII.        $5.00-$20.00
Format IX.          $3.00-$15.00

Picture Cover B. - 1971+
Illustrator: Rudy Nappi
Format IX.          $3.00-$15.00
Format X.           $3.00-$10.00

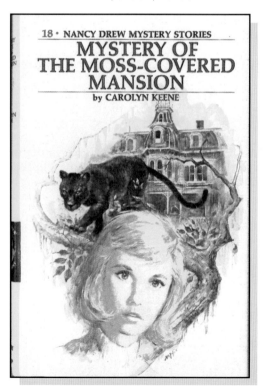

**18**. PC A.

**18**. PC B.

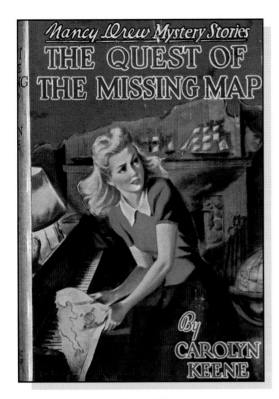

**19**. DJ A.

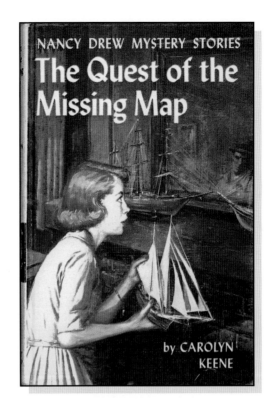

**19**. PC A.

# 19. The Quest of the Missing Map

1942 Edition. 213 Pages.

Buried treasure again. Nancy searches for the other half of a treasure map belonging to Mr. Smith that will show him where a fortune is hidden and perhaps reunite him with his lost twin brother.

1969 Edition. 178 Pages.

The shorter edition is an update of the original story of the treasure island.

    Dust Jacket A. - 1942 - 1961
    Illustrator: Russell H. Tandy
    Format II.        $12.00-$250.00
    Format III.       $8.00-$185.00
    Format IV.        $8.00-$125.00
    Format V.         $5.00-$50.00
    Format VI.        $5.00-$45.00
    Format VII.       $5.00-$40.00

    Picture Cover A. - 1962 - 1968
    Illustrator: Rudy Nappi
    Format VIII.      $5.00-$20.00

    Picture Cover B. - 1969+
    Illustrator: Rudy Nappi
    Format IX.        $3.00-$15.00
    Format X.         $3.00-$10.00

**19**. PC B.

## 20. The Clue in the Jewel Box

1943 Edition. 216 Pages.

Nancy solves two mysteries again. One involves the search for a former queen's grandson; the other is about a secret formula in a "Faber" jewel box. With Nancy's help, Madame Alexandra is reunited with her grandson, Michael, and a secret process for enamel making is found. (All of this is taken from myths surrounding the last Czar of Russia.)

1972 Edition. 181 Pages.

In the abridged and updated version of the tale, Nancy solves the same two problems.

> Dust Jacket A. - 1943 - 1961
> Illustrator: Russell H. Tandy
> Format II.         $12.00-$250.00+
>    (Poor paper is balanced with the
>      fact that this is the last thick
>      printing of the series.)
> Format III.        $8.00-$185.00
> Format IV.        $8.00-$125.00
> Format V.         $5.00-$50.00
> Format VI.        $5.00-$45.00
> Format VII.       $5.00-$40.00
>
> Picture Cover A. - 1962 - 1972
> Illustrator: Rudy Nappi
> Format VIII.      $4.00-$25.00
> Format IX.        $3.00-$15.00
>
> Picture Cover B. - 1972+
> Illustrator: Rudy Nappi
> Format IX.        $3.00-$25.00
>    (Only printing with original text.)
> Format X.         $3.00-$10.00

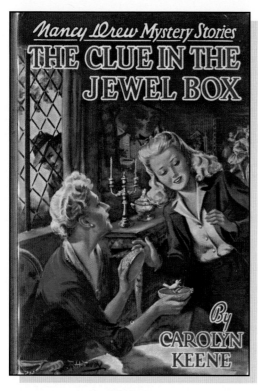

**20**. DJ A.

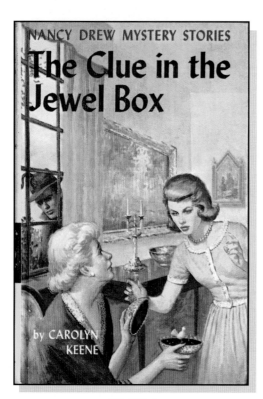

**20**. PC A.

**20**. PC B.

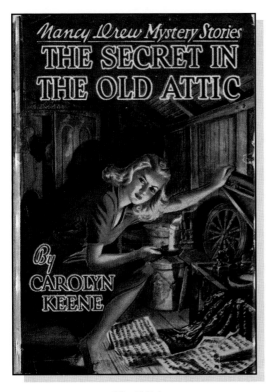

**21.** DJ A.

**21.** PC A.

# 21. The Secret in the Old Attic

1944 Edition. 216 Pages.

On the third floor of "a rambling structure," Nancy searches for unpublished songs written by elderly Mr. March's deceased son. A criminal traps Nancy in the attic with a tarantula whose bite is supposed to kill her.

1970 Edition. 177 Pages.

The story is updated and a major correction is made: The "deadly" spider is now a black widow, as the bite of a tarantula is not fatal.

Dust Jacket A. - 1944 - 1961
Illustrator: Russell H. Tandy
Format III.          $8.00-$150.00
Format IV.          $8.00-$125.00
Format V.           $5.00-$50.00
Format VI.          $5.00-$45.00
Format VII.         $5.00-$40.00

Picture Cover A. - 1962 - 1969
Illustrator: Rudy Nappi
Format VIII.        $4.00-$25.00
Format IX.          $3.00-$20.00

Picture Cover B. - 1970+
Illustrator: Rudy Nappi
Format IX.          $3.00-$15.00
Format X.           $3.00-$10.00

**21.** PC B.

# 22. The Clue in the Crumbling Wall

1945 Edition. 217 Pages.

Several miles up the Muskoka River from River Heights is the ruined estate Heath Castle. Florianna Johnson will lose her claim to the castle if Nancy cannot locate her and a document to prove her right to ownership.

1973 Edition. 181 Pages.

In this adaptation, Nancy risks her life to help Juliana, the new name for the heiress.

Dust Jacket A. - 1945 - 1961
Illustrator: Russell H. Tandy
Format III.        $8.00-$150.00
Format IV.         $8.00-$125.00
Format V.          $5.00-$50.00
Format VI.         $5.00-$45.00
Format VII.        $5.00-$40.00

Picture Cover A. - 1962 - 1973
Illustrator: Rudy Nappi
Format VIII.       $4.00-$20.00
Format IX.         $3.00-$15.00

Picture Cover B. - 1973+
Illustrator: Rudy Nappi
Format IX.         $3.00-$15.00
Format X.          $3.00-$10.00

**22**. DJ A.

**22**. PC A.

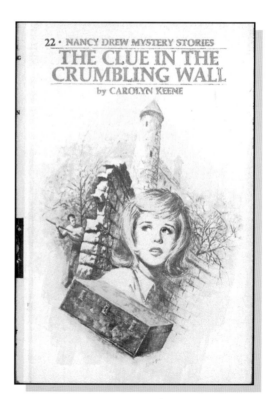

**22**. PC B.

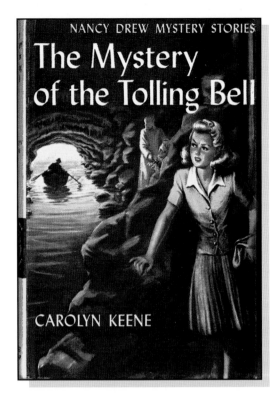

**23**. DJ A/PC A.

**23**. PC B.

# 23. The Mystery of the Tolling Bell

1946 Edition. 213 Pages.

Nancy, Bess and George go to White Cap Bay for vacation. The mysteries there are why did Mr. Drew not show up, what makes a strange bell toll in a seaside cave and what do Mon Coeur cosmetics have to do with this phenomenon?

1973 Edition. **Mystery of the Tolling Bell**. 181 Pages.

Nancy brings swindlers to justice in fewer pages. (This is the same plot, with a title alteration, that actually began with the front cover of the second Picture Cover [Picture Cover B], although the inside contents of the book are the same as the Dust Jacket Version.)

**23**. PC C.

Dust Jacket A. - 1946 - 1961
Illustrator: Russell H. Tandy
Format III.          $8.00-$150.00
Format IV.          $8.00-$125.00
Format V.           $5.00-$50.00
Format VI.          $5.00-$45.00
Format VII.              $5.00-$40.00

Picture Cover A. - 1962 - 1966
(Same as Dust Jacket A)
Format VIII.        $4.00-$25.00

Picture Cover B. - 1966 - 1973
Illustrator:  Rudy Nappi
Format VIII.             $4.00-$20.00
Format IX.          $3.00-$15.00

Picture Cover C. - 1973+
Illustrator:  Rudy Nappi
Format IX.          $3.00-$15.00
Format X.           $3.00-$10.00

## 24. The Clue in the Old Album

1947 Edition. 218 Pages.

When Nancy recovers doll collector Mrs. Struthers' stolen purse, she is asked to search for an important stolen doll. This leads Nancy to a gypsy camp, where she is kidnapped like Beverly Gray was in *Beverly Gray, Junior* (1934).

Note: The dust jacket art is considered the best work of R.H. Tandy, the most beautiful Nancy Drew classic cover, and one of the prettiest interpretations of Nancy.

1977 Edition. 180 Pages.

The revised and updated book is a shorter version of the tale.

**24**. DJ A/PC A.

> Dust Jacket A. - 1947 - 1961
> Illustrator: Russell H. Tandy
> Format V.          $5.00-$50.00
> Format VI.         $5.00-$45.00
> Format VII.        $5.00-$40.00
>
> Picture Cover A. - 1962 - 1965
> (Same as Dust Jacket A)
> Format VIII.       $10.00-$30.00
>
> Picture Cover B. - 1966 - 1976
> Illustrator: Rudy Nappi
> Format VIII.       $3.00-$25.00
> Format IX.         $3.00-$15.00
>
> Picture Cover C. - 1977+
> Illustrator: Rudy Nappi
> Format IX.         $3.00-$15.00
> Format X.          $3.00-$10.00

**24**. PC B.

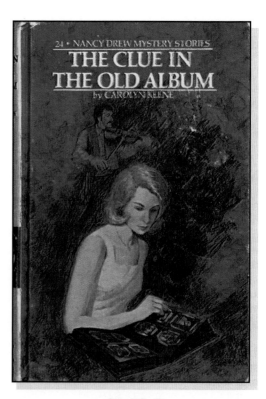

**24**. PC. C.

# 25. The Ghost of Blackwood Hall

1948 Edition. 216 Pages.

In another spooky old house story, Nancy outwits a gang of jewel thieves. To go helps.

1967 Edition. 178 Pages.

The mystery of the house in New Orleans is updated and abridged.

> Dust Jacket A. - 1948 - 1961
> Illustrator: Russell H. Tandy
> Format V.          $5.00-$50.00
> Format VI.         $5.00-$45.00
> Format VII.        $5.00-$40.00
>
> Picture Cover A. - 1962 - 1967
> (Same as Dust Jacket A)
> Format VIII.       $4.00-$25.00
>     1967 Edition   $10.00-$35.00
>
> Picture Cover B. - 1968+
> Illustrator: Rudy Nappi
> Format VIII.       $3.00-$25.00
> Format IX.         $3.00-$15.000
> Format X.          $3.00-$10.00

Note: Both text versions are in Picture Cover A.

# 26. The Clue of the Leaning Chimney

1949 Edition. 212 Pages.

Dick Milton, Bess' cousin, has a valuable Chinese vase stolen from his shop. Nancy finds the vase, a deposit of porcelain clay and a missing father and daughter, all connected with an old porcelain factory.

1967 Edition. 176 Pages.

Nancy finds the building with the leaning chimney in an abridged and shortened version of the story.

> Dust Jacket A. - 1949 - 1961
> Illustrator: Russell H. Tandy
> Format V.          $5.00-$50.00
> Format VI.         $5.00-$45.00
> Format VII.        $5.00-$40.00
>
> Picture Cover A. - 1962 - 1966
> (Same as Dust Jacket A)
> Format VIII.       $10.00-$35.00
>
> Picture Cover B. - 1967+
> Illustrator: Rudy Nappi
> Format VIII.       $10.00-$35.00
> Format IX.         $3.00-$15.00
> Format X.          $3.00-$10.00

Note: This is the last Russell H. Tandy dust jacket and frontispiece.

**25**. DJ A/PC A.

**25**. PC B.

**26**. DJ A/PC A.

**26**. PC B.

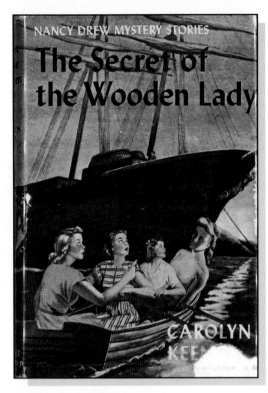

**27**. DJ A/PC A.

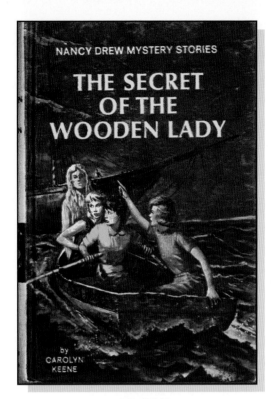

**27**. PC B.

## 27. The Secret of the Wooden Lady

1950 Edition. 213 Pages.

Nancy Drew and her father help Captain Easterly of Boston purchase a haunted ship and restore its lost figurehead.

1967 Edition. 176 Pages.

The title of the ship is cleared and the figurehead found in the updated version of the story.

> Dust Jacket A. - 1950 - 1961
> Illustrator: Bill Gillies
> Format V.      $5.00-$55.00
> Format VI.     $5.00-$45.00
> Format VII.    $5.00-$40.00
>
> Picture Cover A. - 1962 - 1966
> (Same as Dust Jacket A)
> Format VIII.   $3.00-$25.00
>
> Picture Cover B. - 1967+
> Illustrator: Rudy Nappi
> Format VIII.   $5.00-$25.00
> Format IX.     $3.00-$15.00
> Format X.      $3.00-$10.00

Note: In the three 1950 printings and the first 1951 printing of the book, Ned is holding a cigarette in his hand in the frontispiece picture.

## 28. The Clue of the Black Keys

1951 Edition. 214 Pages.

Dr. Terry Scott begs Nancy to help him locate his colleague, Dr. Pitt, who disappeared along with an ancient stone tablet that tells about buried treasure. Nancy travels to the Florida Keys and to Mexico to help the archeologist.

1968 Edition. 174 Pages.

In the condensed version of the story, the episode of Mr. and Mrs. Tino torturing Nancy is omitted. In the synopsis at the front of this edition it states, "Again, Carolyn Keene has woven a suspense-filled story that will thrill her millions of readers."

> Dust Jacket A. - 1951 - 1961
> Illustrator: Bill Gillies
> Format V.      $5.00-$60.00
> Format VI.     $5.00-$45.00
> Format VII.    $5.00-$40.00
>
> Picture Cover A. - 1962 - 1967
> (Same as Dust Jacket A)
> Format VIII.   $3.00-$25.00
>
> Picture Cover B. - 1968+
> Illustrator: Rudy Nappi
> Format VIII.   $3.00-$30.00
> Format IX.     $3.00-$15.00
> Format X.      $3.00-$10.00

29. DJ A/PC A.

29. PC B.

28. DJ A/PC A.

28. PC B.

## 29. The Mystery at the Ski Jump

1952 Edition. 212 Pages.

A swindler is using the name Nancy Drew to dupe people into purchasing her stolen furs. Nancy travels to Montreal in Canada to track the thieves and at a skating competition hears her name announced as a contestant. In Chapter XXV, Nancy clears up all the problems and mistakes.

1968 Edition. **Mystery at the Ski Jump**. 176 Pages.

The updated book is "another thrilling Carolyn Keene mystery" with an altered title.

Dust Jacket A. - 1952 - 1962
Illustrator: Bill Gillies
Format V.              $5.00-$65.00
Format VI.             $5.00-$45.00
Format VII.            $5.00-$40.00

Picture Cover A. - 1962 - 1967
(Same as Dust Jacket A)
Format VIII.           $3.00-$25.00

Picture Cover B. - 1968+
Illustrator: Rudy Nappi
Format VIII.           $3.00-$35.00
Format IX.             $3.00-$15.00
Format X.              $3.00-$10.00

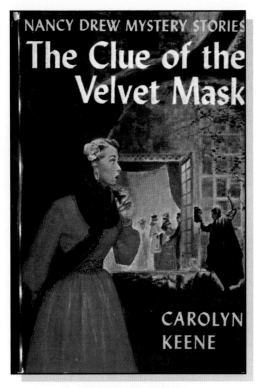

**30**. DJ A/PC A.

**30**. PC B.

## 30. The Clue of the Velvet Mask

1953 Edition. 211 Pages.

When Nancy and Ned went to a masquerade party dressed in Spanish folk costumes, they encountered a gang of art and jewel thieves. With some help, these culprits were unmasked.

1969 Edition. 177 Pages.

This is the same story in a shortened version.

    Dust Jacket A. - 1953 - 1961
    Illustrator: Rudy Nappi
    Format VI.    $5.00-$50.00
    Format VII.    $5.00-$45.00

    Picture Cover A. - 1962 - 1968
    (Same as Dust Jacket A)
    Format VIII.    $3.00-$25.00

    Picture Cover B. - 1968+
    Illustrator: Rudy Nappi
    Format IX.    $3.00-$15.00
    Format X.    $3.00-$10.00

## 31. The Ringmaster's Secret

1953 Edition. 214 Pages.

Nancy acquires a bracelet that had belonged to a queen and this leads her to help Lolita, the queen of the circus aerialists, in her search for her real mother.

1974 Edition. 178 Pages.

The condensed version of the same story has minor changes.

    Dust Jacket A. - 1953 - 1961
    Illustrator: Rudy Nappi
    Format VI.    $5.00-$50.00
    Format VII.    $5.00-$45.00

    Picture Cover A. - 1962 - 1973
    (Same as Dust Jacket A)
    Format VIII.    $3.00-$25.00
    Format IX.    $3.00-$15.00

    Picture Cover B. - 1974+
    Illustrator: Rudy Nappi
    Format IX.    $3.00-$15.00
    Format X.    $3.00-$10.00

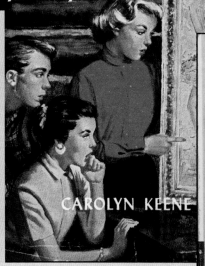

**32**. DJ A/PC A.

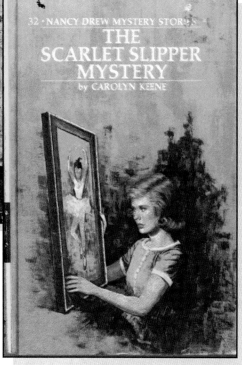

**32**. PC B.

**31**. DJ A/PC A.

**31**. PC B.

## 32. The Scarlet Slipper Mystery

1954 Edition. 212 Pages.

Nancy meets ballet dancers Helene and Henri Fontaine, refugees from Centrovia, who now run a dance school. They search for missing jewels.

1974 Edition. 179 Pages.

The abridged version.

> Dust Jacket A. - 1954 - 1961
> Illustrator: Rudy Nappi
> Format VI.          $5.00-$50.00
> Format VII.         $5.00-$45.00
>
> Picture Cover A. - 1962 - 1973
> (Same as Dust Jacket A)
> Format VIII.        $3.00-$25.00
> Format IX.          $3.00-$15.00
>
> Picture Cover B. - 1974+
> Illustrator: Rudy Nappi
> Format IX.          $3,00-$15.00
> Format X.           $3.00-$10.00

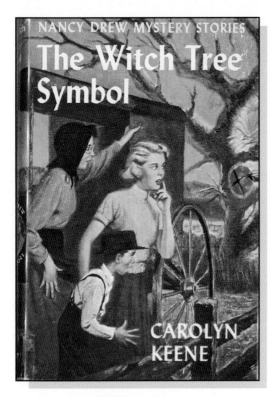

**33**. DJ A/PC A.

**33**. PC B.

# 33. The Witch Tree Symbol

1955 Edition. 213 Pages.

Nancy travels to Pennsylvania Dutch country to search for missing furniture and to help Manda Kreutz locate her parents.

1975 Edition. 179 Pages.

The condensed version of the mystery.

> Dust Jacket A. - 1955 - 1961
> Illustrator: Rudy Nappi
> Format VI.          $5.00-$50.00
> Format VII.         $5.00-$45.00
>
> Picture Cover A. - 1962 - 1974
> (Same as Dust Jacket A)
> Format VIII.        $3.00-$25.00
> Format IX.          $3.00-$15.00
>
> Picture Cover B. - 1975+
> Illustrator: Rudy Nappi
> Format IX.          $3.00-$15.00
> Format X.           $3.00-$10.00

# 34. The Hidden Window Mystery

1956 Edition. 214 Pages.

Nancy and her chums travel to Charlottesville, Virginia, to search for a rare stained-glass window that has been stolen. A ghost bothers the girls in an old southern mansion.

Note: This is the last Classic Nancy Drew book with twenty-five chapters.

1975 Edition. 179 Pages.

This is the last Classic Nancy Drew book that was abridged.

> Dust Jacket A. - 1957 - 1961
> Illustrator: Rudy Nappi
> Format VI.          $5.00-$50.00
> Format VII.         $5.00-$45.00
>
> Picture Cover A. - 1962 - 1974
> (Same as Dust Jacket A)
> Format VIII.        $3.00-$25.00
> Format IX.          $3.00-$15.00
>
> Picture Cover B. - 1975+
> Illustrator: Rudy Nappi
> Format IX.          $3.00-$15.00
> Format X.           $3.00-$12.00

Note: This is also the last Classic Nancy Drew book to have more than one cover design.

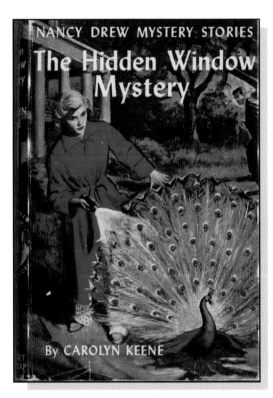

**34**. DJ A/PC A.

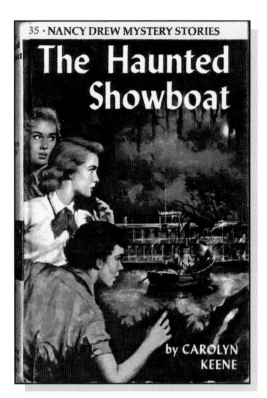

**35**. DJ A/PC A.

**34**. PC B.

## 35. The Haunted Showboat

1957 Edition. 184 Pages.

Nancy, George and Bess go to New Orleans for Mardi Gras. The mysteries involve an abandoned showboat that may be haunted.

> Dust Jacket A. - 1958 - 1961
> Illustrator: Rudy Nappi
> Format VI.          $5.00-$70.00
> Format VII.         $5.00-$60.00
>
> Picture Cover A. - 1962+
> (Same as Dust Jacket A)
> Format VIII.        $3.00-$25.00
> Format IX.          $3.00-$15.00
> Format X.           $3.00-$10.00

36. DJ A/PC A.

37. DJ A/PC A.

38. DJ A/PC A.

## 36. The Secret of the Golden Pavilion

1959 Edition. 184 Pages.

Nancy Drew and her friends travel to Hawaii and solve a troubling puzzle at Honolulu's Golden Pavilion.

    Dust Jacket A. - 1959 - 1961
    Illustrator: Rudy Nappi
    Format VII.    $5.00-$75.00+

    Picture Cover A. - 1962+
    (Same as Dust Jacket A)
    Format VIII.    $3.00-$25.00
    Format IX.    $3.00-$15.00
    Format X.    $3.00-$10.00

## 37. The Clue in the Old Stagecoach

1960 Edition. 180 Pages.

Mrs. Strook asks Nancy and her two best friends to go to the town of Bridgeford and investigate an old stagecoach that contains a family secret.

    Dust Jacket A. - 1960 - 1961
    Illustrator: Rudy Nappi
    Format VII.    $5.00-$80.00+

    Picture Cover A. - 1962+
    (Same as Dust Jacket A)
    Format VIII.    $3.00-$25.00
    Format IX.    $3.00-$15.00
    Format X.    $3.00-$10.00

## 38. The Mystery of the Fire Dragon

1961 Edition. 182 Pages.

Ned is in Hong Kong as an exchange student. Nancy and her friends travel there to solve the mystery of the disappearance of the Chinese girl, Che Chi, and a stolen manuscript.

    Dust Jacket A. - 1961
    Illustrator: Rudy Nappi
    Format VII.    $10.00-$100.00+

    Picture Cover A. - 1962+
    (Same as Dust Jacket A)
    Format VIII.    $3.00-$25.00
    Format IX.    $3.00-$15.00
    Format X.    $3.00-$10.00

Note: This is the last Classic Nancy Drew book with a dust jacket.

## 39. The Clue of the Dancing Puppet

1962 Edition. 177 Pages.

A life-size puppet is haunting the Van Pelt mansion, the site of the Footlighters' amateur theatrical productions. Nancy joins the show and solves the puzzles.

    Picture Cover A. - 1962+
    Illustrator: Rudy Nappi
    Format VIII.    $3.00-$25.00
    Format IX.    $3.00-$15.00
    Format X.    $3.00-$15.00

## 40. The Moonstone Castle Mystery

1963 Edition. 178 Pages.

Nancy, Bess and George investigate a castle with a drawbridge in connection with the disappearance of the granddaughter of a missionary couple. These events are associated with the anonymous gift of a moonstone gem that Nancy received in the mail.

    Picture Cover A. - 1963+
    Illustrator: Rudy Nappi
    Format VIII.    $3.00-$25.00
    Format IX.    $3.00-$15.00
    Format X.    $3.00-$10.00

## 41. The Clue of the Whistling Bagpipes

1964 Edition. 177 Pages.

Nancy is warned not to go to Scotland with her father and her two good friends. She goes to the Highlands anyhow to solve the mystery of a missing family treasure. On a dark night, she dresses in a tartan and plays the bagpipes as part of her plan to regain a flock of stolen sheep.

    Picture Cover A. - 1964+
    Illustrator: Rudy Nappi
    Format VIII.    $3.00-$25.00
    Format IX.    $3.00-$15.00
    Format X.    $3.00-$10.00

**39**. PC A.

**40**. PC A.

**41**. PC A.

**42**. PC A.

**43**. PC A.

**44**. PC A.

## 42. The Phantom of Pine Hill

1965 Edition. 176 Pages.

Nancy and her two close friends travel to Emerson University to visit Ned Nickerson. When their motel reservation is not honored, the girls are invited to stay at the mansion of the uncle of a professor. Nancy solves the mysteries of a phantom at the mansion, a sunken ship and lost treasures.

Picture Cover A. - 1965+
Illustrator: Rudy Nappi
Format VIII.     $3.00-$25.00
Format IX.     $3.00-$15.00
Format X.     $3.00-$10.00

## 43. The Mystery of the 99 Steps

1966 Edition. 176 Pages.

Nancy and her friends travel to France to search for a stairway of ninety-nine mysterious steps to solve the mystery of a friend's dream and her father is there to handle the problem of some missing securities. The two cases are intertwined, leading the girls to chateau country in the Loire Valley.

Picture Cover A. - 1966+
Illustrator: Rudy Nappi
Format VIII.     $3.00-$25.00
Format IX.     $3.00-$15.00
Format X.     $3.00-$10.00

## 44. The Clue in the Crossword Cipher

1967 Edition. 177 Pages.

Nancy, George and Bess are invited to travel to Peru by Carla Ponce to help solve the mystery of a wooden plaque in cipher that leads to a hidden treasure. The girls also visit the ancient sites of Cuzco and Machu Picchu during their investigations.

Picture Cover A. - 1967+
Illustrator: Rudy Nappi
Format VIII.     $3.00-$25.00
Format IX.     $3.00-$15.00
Format X.     $3.00-$10.00

## 45. The Spider Sapphire Mystery

1968 Edition. 176 Pages.

Nancy goes to East Africa on safari to solve the mystery of the theft of a valuable sapphire because her father's client, a maker of synthetic gems, is accused of stealing it.

> Picture Cover A. - 1968+
> Illustrator: Rudy Nappi
> Format VIII.     $3.00-$25.00+
> Format IX.      $3.00-$15.00
> Format X.       $3.00-$10.00

## 46. The Invisible Intruder

1969 Edition. 175 Pages.

Nancy is warned by telephone to "forget the ghost hunt" when she and her friends set out to investigate five different places that are reputed to be haunted. Nancy outwits her enemy in another weird mansion.

> Picture Cover A. - 1969+
> Illustrator: Rudy Nappi
> Format IX.      $3.00-$15.00
> Format X.       $3.00-$10.00

## 47. The Mysterious Mannequin

1970 Edition. 178 Pages.

Nancy sets out to track down a mannequin that is missing from Farouk Tahmasp's rug shop. She and all her friends travel to Istanbul to solve the mystery.

> Picture Cover A. - 1970+
> Illustrator: Rudy Nappi
> Format IX.      $3.00-$15.00
> Format X.       $3.00-$10.00

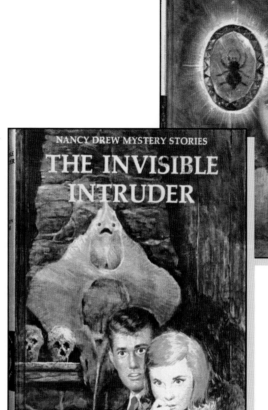

**45**. PC A.

**46**. PC A.

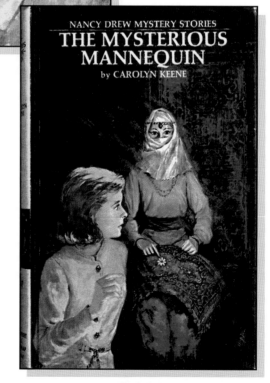

**47**. PC A.

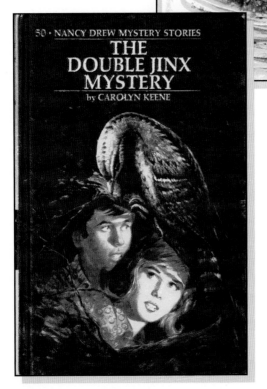

**48**. PC A.

**49**. PC A.

**50**. PC A.

## 48. The Crooked Banister

1971 Edition. 179 Pages.

Nancy and her friends spend an exciting weekend in an unusual zigzag-designed house where they are endangered by a robot and "have several hair-raising adventures."

Picture Cover A. - 1971+
Illustrator: Rudy Nappi
Format IX. $3.00-$15.00
Format X. $3.00-$10.00

## 49. The Secret of Mirror Bay

1972 Edition. 178 Pages.

Aunt Eloise Drew invites Nancy and her friends to Mirror Bay, near Cooperstown, New York. Nancy solves mysteries of phantoms, mistaken identities and hoaxes.

Picture Cover A. - 1972+
Illustrator: Rudy Nappi
Format IX. $3.00-$15.00
Format X. $3.00-$10.00

## 50. The Double Jinx Mystery

1973 Edition. 180 Pages.

A stuffed bird, which Nancy identifies as a wryneck woodpecker, is placed on the Drew's front lawn. This leads Nancy to the problem of saving a rare bird farm from demolition because an apartment complex is to be built on its site.

Picture Cover A. - 1973+
Illustrator: Rudy Nappi
Format IX. $3.00-$15.00
Format X. $3.00-$10.00

## 51. Mystery of the Glowing Eye

1974 Edition. 181 Pages.

Ned Nickerson is kidnapped! Nancy, George and Bess rush to Emerson University to rescue him.

    Picture Cover A. - 1974+
    Illustrator: Rudy Nappi
    Format IX.        $3.00-$15.00
    Format X.        $3.00-$10.00

## 52. The Secret of the Forgotten City

1975 Edition. 180 Pages.

Nancy and her friends travel to Nevada to join a college dig to hunt for gold. A Native American woman helps the group rescue the area from a thief who also wants the treasure.

    Picture Cover A. - 1975+
    Illustrator: Rudy Nappi
    Format IX.        $3.00-$15.00
    Format X.        $3.00-$10.00

## 53. The Sky Phantom

1976 Edition. 180 Pages.

Nancy takes flying lessons; George and Bess perfect their horseback riding skills. All join forces to catch a plane hijacker and a thief.

    Picture Cover A. - 1976+
    Illustrator: Rudy Nappi
    Format IX.        $3.00-$15.00
    Format X.        $3.00-$10.00

**51**. PC A.

**52**. PC A.

**53**. PC A.

**54**. PC A.

**55**. PC A.

**56**. PC A.

## 54. The Strange Message in the Parchment

1977 Edition. 180 Pages.

After a sheep farmer purchases a set of paintings on parchment he receives a strange telephone call telling him to decipher the messages on them. Nancy, her friends and even Togo solve several puzzles linked to this.

> Picture Cover A. - 1977+
> Illustrator: Rudy Nappi
> Format IX.　　　$3.00-$15.00
> Format X.　　　$3.00-$10.00

## 55. Mystery of Crocodile Island

1978 Edition. 180 Pages.

Nancy's father asks her to help a friend worried about poachers on a Florida Island. Nancy, Ned, George and Bess encounter many dangers before the problem is solved.

> Picture Cover A. - 1978+
> Illustrator: Rudy Nappi
> Format IX.　　　$3.00-$15.00
> Format X.　　　$3.00-$10.00

## 56. The Thirteenth Pearl

1979 Edition. 179 Pages.

Nancy is asked to search for a valuable pearl necklace that has been stolen. She and her father travel to Japan, where Nancy disguises herself as a Japanese girl, to work on the case. Back in River Heights, Nancy and Ned are kidnapped because of her persistence in locating the necklace and the involvement of a dishonest gem company.

> Picture Cover A. - 1979+
> Illustrator: Rudy Nappi
> Format IX.　　　$3.00-$20.00
> 　W/*Triple Hoax* advertised on
> 　　Page 178　　$40.00
> Format X.　　　$3.00-$10.00

Note: All the covers by Rudy Nappi up to this one seem to be paintings on a smooth surface. The art on *The Thirteenth Pearl* appears to be pastel chalk on a textured surface.

# CHAPTER 4

# Judy Bolton Mystery Stories

**Left:** The Austin Dam, near Austin, Pennsylvania, in June 1998. The concrete portion of the dam has been standing in this position since it burst in 1911.

Bette Ann Axe at the base of the Austin Dam, June 1998.

Potter County, Pennsylvania, is larger than the state of Rhode Island but the entire county has only about 17,000 inhabitants. This rural location in north-central Pennsylvania is the setting of the thirty-eight Judy Bolton books by Margaret Sutton.

Sutton was still in her twenties when she began the series and she remembered her youth clearly, as it was the source for many of her stories. She claimed that all her books were "based on something that actually happened," and they were advertised this way. Unlike many authors of juvenile fiction at the time, Margaret Sutton avoided using exotic locales as settings for her tales and never wrote about places that she had not seen herself. Although the majority of the books are set in and around Coudersport, the county seat of Potter county, (called Farringdon in the novels), Margaret Sutton's Judy Bolton had adventures that surpassed those who lived more sophisticated lives, such as Beverly Gray, who traveled all over the world, or Nancy Drew, who solved dozens of mysteries a year. As with all mystery novels meant for young people, coincidence plays a large role in the plots, but the fantastic and unreal is kept at a minimum. Judy was never kidnapped by Gypsies and she seldom traveled far from home. The first twenty books take place primarily in rural north-central Pennsylvania but it is amazing how many criminal types Judy encountered near Dry Brook Hollow (based on Odin, Pennsylvania, whose population was always tiny) and the relationship that many of the characters and their problems had with New York City.

The inspiration for the first book in the series, *The Vanishing Shadow*, was the biggest event that ever occurred in Potter County. This was the Austin Flood of 1911, which took place when a large dam broke three miles downstream from the house where Margaret Sutton was born. The Austin Dam was completed in 1909 on Freeman Run by the Bayless Pulp and Paper Company for water power and for flood control in the deep, narrow valley upstream

from the mill, which took advantage of the surrounding forests. The concrete dam was 534 feet long and 43 feet high and held an estimated 500,000,000 gallons of water. The sudden bursting of the dam was believed to have occurred because the cement on the outside of it dried too fast, causing a large, unhardened mass to remain inside. On September 30, 1911, the lake behind the dam was full from recent rains. A huge plug of concrete about eight by ten feet was blown out of the dam, which quickly broke clear through, sending a boiling "soup" of logs downstream. Two towns, Austin and Costello, were practically wiped off the map and at least seventy-eight people, some of whose bodies were never recovered, were dead. This catastrophe was the basis of the fictional plot of the first Judy Bolton Mystery.

In each following Mystery, Judy Bolton, with the help of her many friends and family members, solves riddles, problems and secrets. Many of the settings are spooky old houses, a staple in juvenile fiction, but Sutton's plot devices seldom lack excitement, even though they are about simple things, such as locating the relatives of an orphan. I feel that the stories featuring ten-year-old Roberta Dunn, who appears in six adventures (Volumes 16 through 21), represent Margaret Sutton's writing at its height. The book after the exit of Roberta, *The Spirit of Fog Island*, is also one of the best mysteries of all but from that point they decline in originality and quality.

Although each mystery is complete in itself, there is a chronological progression from *The Vanishing Shadow* (1932) to the last book, *The Secret of the*

67

*Sand Castle* (Volume 38, 1967). During this time, six years have passed and Judy has gone from a fifteen-year-old girl to a married woman. Some books last only a few days (three days each for *The Clue in the Ruined Castle, The Haunted Fountain* and *The Pledge of the Twin Knights*) and others over two months (sixty-four days for *The Unfinished House*, which was also the longest book of all at 250 pages).

Although the Judy Bolton Mysteries were advertised by publisher Grosset & Dunlap as girls' books, I always felt that Sutton's writing appealed to a wider audience. The last dozen or so volumes in the Judy Bolton series are "dummied down" for younger readers than they were originally intended for, which was no doubt a dictate from the publisher and a detriment to the series, although it probably helped to prolong it.

The Judy Bolton Mysteries endured for thirty-five years before the publisher canceled the series. This is the longest-lasting juvenile series written by a single author. In the course of the series, Dr. and Mrs. Bolton's daughter, Judy, moves from flood-destroyed Roulsville to the larger town of Farringdon where she is aided in her mystery-solving by her brother, Horace; her childhood friend, Peter (who becomes an FBI agent and whom she later marries), and his sister, Honey; friends Lorraine Lee, Arthur Farringdon-Pett and his sister, Lois; Irene Lang; Pauline Faulkner from New York City; Judy's cousin, Roxy, from Cleveland; and others who appear in more than one book. The parents and grandparents of many of these are also featured in the mysteries. Another of Judy's helpers at mystery-solving is the cat Blackberry that Peter gave her in the first book.

At the end of the series Judy is living in Dry Brook Hollow in the house that her grandmother left her in her will and which was based on the house in Odin, Pennsylvania, in which Margaret Sutton was born and is still there. I feel that the real strength of the Judy Bolton Mysteries is that they are about normal people and primarily about natural events that an average young person would encounter.

## Margaret Sutton

Margaret Sutton was born Rachel Irene Beebe in Odin, Pennsylvania, January 22, 1903, the youngest of three children of Stella Andrews Beebe and Victor L. Beebe. The Beebe family later moved to nearby Coudersport, Pennsylvania, where Margaret left school at age sixteen. By 1920, she had graduated from Rochester Business Institute and later worked

Margaret Sutton from a Grosset & Dunlap book jacket back, 1930s.

at various jobs in Rochester, Detroit, Cleveland, Chicago and New York City, where she met William H. Sutton, whom she married in 1924.

William Sutton was a widower who was thirteen years older than Margaret and he had a six-year-old daughter, Dorothy. Margaret has cited many times that the creation of her most famous works, the Judy Bolton books, originated with stories that she originally told to Dorothy and later wrote down. By 1930, Dorothy was reading the Ruth Fielding series and Margaret decided to turn her "Melissa of Dry Brook Hollow" stories, which were based on experiences from her childhood, into published books. Through an agent she placed the first four Judy Bolton books with Grosset & Dunlap, who changed the author's name from Rachel to Margaret (which she used ever since) and the fictional heroine's from Melissa to Judy Bolton. The Dedication in the first three Judy Bolton books is simply "To Dorothy."

I first met Margaret Sutton in person in June of 1998 at the library in Coudersport where she spoke of her life and her work. Her family used this event as an occasion for a reunion. Margaret's and William Sutton's three daughters, Eleanor, Marjorie and Linda, and their son Tommy were there, along with Dorothy. Before she began her talk, Margaret Sutton said, "Dorothy, come up here and sit beside me. You have always been my favorite." Dorothy, who was about eighty, obeyed.

The decade of the 1930s was Margaret Sutton's most prolific period. In 1932, her first four Judy Bolton books were published; two more came out the following year, and one each year after that. In 1936, the three volumes of "The Magic Makers," a new series, were released. In 1938, it was *Heidi Grows Up*, which she revised extensively from the manuscript of Charles Tritten, "Johanna Spyri's translator," who gets author credit for the book, and in 1939, *Heidi's Children*, which she wrote entirely and which also has Tritten's name on the cover. Also in 1939 was *Lollypop: the True Story of a Little Dog*. All these books were published by Grosset & Dunlap. At this time also was *Kay Darcy and the Mystery Hideout*, published for Whitman in 1937 under the pseudonym Irene Ray and *Baby's Day in Rhymes and Pictures*, a collaboration with Pelagie Doane, and *Summer on the Farm* in 1938, for Grosset & Dunlap.

In 1944 and 1945, Dodd, Mead & Company published two of

Sutton's books in another series that did not continue. These were *Gail Gardner Wins Her Cap* and *Gail Gardner, Junior Cadet Nurse.* During the 1940s, she did two other books for Grosset & Dunlap: *A Shepherd Boy of Australia* (1941) and *Two Boys of the Ohio Valley* (1943). Other books of this decade were *Jemima, Daughter of Daniel Boone* (Charles Scribner's Sons, 1942), *Tommy True, a Little Boy Who Was Hungry* (Oxford University Press, 1942) and *The Haunted Apartment* (Dodd, Mead & Company, 1946).

Sutton's non-Judy Bolton books of the 1950s were *Who Will Play With Me?* (Grosset & Dunlap, 1953) and *Palace Wagon Family* (Alfred A. Knopf, Inc., 1957). Her other non-Judy book was *The Weed Walk* (G.P. Putnam's Sons, 1965). The last Judy Bolton Mystery was published in 1967.

William Sutton died in 1965. In 1975, Margaret married Everett Hunting, whom she had known in the early 1920s before her first marriage, and moved to Berkeley, California. Later the couple settled in a nursing home in Lock Haven, Pennsylvania, where Mr. Hunting died in 1993. Margaret Sutton later moved to another care facility in Lock Haven, where she recently suffered a major debilitating stroke.

When I saw Margaret Sutton at her program in the Coudersport Library, the last thing she talked

John Axe received this picture from Margaret Sutton in February 1952.

John Axe with Margaret Sutton in June 1998 at the Coudersport, Pennsylvania, library. *Photograph by Bette Ann Axe.*

about after speaking for about three hours was to confide in all present that she was going to return to California, live on the beach and begin a new series of books. Her daughter, standing behind her, mouthed the words, "It's not happening." But Margaret Sutton is the sort of person who had the imagination to write thirty-eight Judy Bolton Mysteries and many other books, all of which are still appreciated.

## Pelagie Doane

The dust jackets of the first nineteen Judy Bolton books were illustrated by Pelagie Doane. She is one of the few illustrators of series books to have her name on the dust jacket, along with that of the author. Even Russell H. Tandy, who did the early Nancy Drew books, didn't. The inside dust jacket flap of *Trailer Trio* (1942) by Emma Atkins Jacobs, published by John C. Winston Company states, "Pelagie Doane was selected to illustrate this delightful story because she is noted for her accurate and clever interpretations of the 'younger set.'" William Collins Sons and Co. Ltd. of London has more information about her on the dust flap of the books she illustrated than there is about the authors. From *Hans Brinker or The Silver Skates* (1958 edition): "Her fresh, charming style of child portrayal appeals tremendously to children of all ages."

Pelagie Doane was born on April 11, 1906, in Palmyra, New Jersey; she died December 9, 1966. She trained initially as an interior decorator and the first commercial art she sold was used for greeting

cards. The first book she illustrated was *Mary Paxon, Her Book*, published by Doubleday in 1931. She did the covers and internal illustrations for about seventy Grosset & Dunlap books and about as many for various other publishers. Some of the series other than the Judy Bolton Mysteries she did for Grosset

Pelagie Doane from a Collins of London dust jacket.

& Dunlap are the Maida books, the Melody Lane Series, the three Heidi books, the Five Little Peppers series and the Louisa May Alcott books. She also

Pelagie Doane dust jacket for Collins, 1970. (Margaret Sutton wrote *Heidi's Children*, which was first published in 1939.)

**I. Fashion-type (early 1930s).** The figures are elongated and stylized. There is a tendency for people to be dressed in a formal way, although the majority of them are teenagers. Judy Bolton is shown in high school wearing high-heeled shoes and her hair is carefully marcelled. The Melody Lane books, at that time, have these same elements in the illustrations.

**II. Cartoon-type (late 1930s).** The illustrations look like they were done very quickly. They had to be, as this was Pelagie Doane's most productive period during which she did hundreds of paintings for books each year. Only an expert can work so quickly and achieve positive results. Examples of this style are found in the early volumes of the Five Little Peppers series and *Two Little Women and Treasure House.*

**III. Realism (1940s).** There are three distinct types of this:

**A.** Stiff and formal. The dust jackets and frontispieces of the Louisa May Alcott books are examples of this, in contrast to the relaxed posing in the drawings of people on the endpapers.

**B.** Drawings that were colored in with pale watercolor. In these works, the people, mostly children, have an animated look. Examples are *A Child's Garden of Verses* (1942) with illustrations that look like the work of Berta Hummel and *Just Like Me* (1946).

**C.** A natural look. This style is reminiscent of some of the work of Norman Rockwell. Books that have these Doane illustrations are the Collins *Heidi* books, the last four Five Little Peppers books and her last Judy Bolton book.

illustrated many books that she wrote, the majority of which were of a religious nature, such as *A Small Child's Bible* (1946), in which the picture helps the child remember the story.

Pelagie Doane had many different styles of artwork. She was influenced by illustration trends of the different periods in which she worked for more than thirty years. Sometimes it is difficult to determine if a picture is hers unless it is credited. She signed her work with her name in script or just initialed it "pd." (Often the signature is cut off the page when the picture is printed.) There are some stylistic devices used consistently in her early work. In the first eleven Judy Bolton books, all the people in the illustrations are seen in full-view. More often than not, they are shown in profile and they tend to lean forwards. In the first three Judy Bolton books, Judy is shown seated on the cover and in the first two she is in almost the same position. Greens and reds dominate the color scheme.

In many ways, it seems as if the artwork of Pelagie Doane developed and became more polished and finished looking as it progressed over the years, which is not to say that her early work did not have a professional quality to it. She, more than any other illustrator of children's literature, had several distinct styles:

The Judy Bolton books illustrated by Pelagie Doane go through this progression of change. From *The Vanishing Shadow* (Volume 1) to *The Unfinished House* (Volume 11), her Judy is rendered in the "Fashion Style"; *The Midnight Visitor* (Volume 12) through *The Secret of the Musical Tree* (Volume 19) are done in the "Realistic Style," with the last one the most natural looking, although Judy is depicted too tall in relation to the three little girls with her. The glossy internal illustrations from the earliest printings of the Judy books were also done originally as paintings although they were printed in black and white. They are done in the original Pelagie Doane style. Some of them (the frontispieces to *The Haunted Attic* and *The Unfinished House*, for example) were redone as more realistic line drawings for the editions of the late 1940s, retaining the original scene but updating clothing and hairstyles, as Tandy did for the Nancy Drew books of the same time period.

During the 1950s and 1960s, Pelagie Doane concentrated on the books that she wrote and illustrated. When the first eight Judy Bolton books were issued with new dust jacket artwork in the 1950s, new artists were hired. Some of these books have interesting covers, but none are as evocative as the Pelagie Doane originals which sold many thousands of Judy Bolton books.

# The Judy Bolton Books

The first Judy Bolton books from Grosset & Dunlap were produced in the same manner as the early Nancy Drew series. Instead of "thick" blue bindings, like the Nancy Drews or red like the Hardy Boys, the Judy Bolton books had light green cloth covers. Like other Grosset & Dunlap series books at the time, the books were about 1-1/4 inches thick.

The first ten volumes in the Judy Bolton series (1932 to 1937) had four black and white pictures inside, printed on glossy paper. These were from paintings by Pelagie Doane which came from originals that were undoubtedly done in full color and were in the same style as the dust jacket designs at the time. The first of these "internals" was the "frontispiece," which depicted some part of the action of the book. The other three pictures were distributed evenly in the book and depicted an action sequence told about in the story near to where the picture appeared.

Volumes 11 through 15 (1938 to 1942) still had thick light green bindings but, inside the books, the only picture was the frontispiece which, by Volume 13, was a line drawing on plain paper instead of a painting printed in black and white. By about 1941, the books were not quite as thick as they had been previously, due to a lighter weight paper inside. After 1954, along with the frontispiece in each new book, there were multiple line drawings (Volumes 26 to 38 and the revision of Volume 1 in 1964).

In 1943, the Judy Bolton books were produced in a more economical way, due to rising costs in publishing and shortages in materials because of the exigencies of World War II. The hard covers were now a dark green simulated cloth or leather, which does not wear as well as the former cover boards. The dust jackets were still the same quality as they had always been, but the ones that were used on reprinted books of earlier volumes did not fit properly, as the spine was designed for a book that was about 1/4 inch thicker. The paper inside the Judy Bolton books (and other Grosset & Dunlap books) from about 1943 to about 1948 was highly acidic "war paper," that has by now darkened considerably and is quite brittle.

By the late 1940s, the frontispieces were dropped from the first eleven books, except for *The Haunted Attic* and *The Voices in the Suitcase*, which had newly drawn pictures in them, and *The Yellow Phantom*, which had used the last original internal instead of the original frontispiece and then had a new line-drawn picture. Presumably the reason that Grosset & Dunlap dropped these frontispieces is because they looked dated by the end of the 1940s, yet the original dust jacket pictures that showed the characters wearing early 1930s styles continued to be used until the first eight were redone in the early 1950s.

There were no new Judy Bolton books in 1944

and 1945, although the earlier volumes of the series were presumably reprinted. From 1946 to 1948, the hard covers were an orange-red or salmon color. By 1947, the endpapers were the "Haunted House" design instead of the original Pelagie Doane endpapers that showed Judy descending a staircase and carrying a flashlight. The first endpapers were in lavender and later in blue, brown and other colors. The Haunted House ones were a burgundy color printed on white paper. By 1948, a Haunted House design was also shown on the hard front cover instead of the square picture silhouette of Judy peering around a tree that had been used since the inception of the series.

The bright red hard cover was introduced in 1948 and continued until the introduction of the "tweed" cover of 1952 to 1963, the one used over the longest span of time. The covers called tweed are a reddish-brownish color with dark and light tones in it. The stock used is a form of composition board with an appearance that looks like cloth. This cover stock is the least durable of all the Judy Bolton books, as its top layer is a thin paper that easily wears or lifts off.

The last style of hard cover Judy Bolton books from Grosset & Dunlap is the picture cover books of 1963 to 1967. These books have the cover picture printed on the front surface on a paper-covered composition board that has a canvas look to it, as did the tweed covers, although it is a more durable surface that can be cleaned. The endpapers are either the Haunted House design or a third design, which is a black line drawing on white paper of Judy with two little girls, which was also used on the last two books printed with dust jackets (Volumes 33 and 34). It is believed that three books do not exist in the picture cover format. They are *The Phantom Friend*, *The Discovery at the Dragon's Mouth* and *The Secret Quest*.

In 1967, the Judy Bolton Mysteries came to an end, although Margaret Sutton had further volumes in the series planned. The same year, Grosset & Dunlap, in a division of the company called Tempo, published paperback editions of the first three books in the series, which had been revised for this format. In 1968, a revised edition of Volume 4 was produced. It appears as if Grosset & Dunlap was attempting to prolong the series. Apparently the paperback project was not successful because it was quickly canceled. These four Judy Bolton books have a posed photograph of a startled looking young girl on the cover, but the design is not attractive or interesting and the lack of a real scene or setting would not cause a young person to develop an interest in the book. Nor were there pictures inside. I think that it was also a mistake not to promote the series as books for both girls and boys, to widen the market as the Spanish publisher of the Judy Bolton mysteries did.

# JUDY BOLTON BOOK FORMATS

## Grosset & Dunlap

I. 1932 - 1937
   #1 - #10, including first editions #1 - #10
   Thick light-green cloth cover
   Small square picture
   Lavender eps by Pelagie Doane
   Glossy frontis
   Three glossy internals
   White spine dj
   Good paper

II. 1938 - 1942
   #1 - #15, including first editions #11 - #15
   Thick light-green cover
   Small square picture
   Lavender eps by Pelagie Doane
   Glossy frontis
   #13 has newspaper photo frontis
   #14 and #15 have plain frontis
   White spine dj
   Good paper

III. 1943 - 1946
   #1 - #17, including first editions #16 - #17
   Thin emerald (or dark green) cover
   Small square picture
   Lavender or blue eps by Pelagie Doane
   #16 white spine dj; #17 wrap dj
   (Reprints have the original white spine djs)
   War papers
Variations: various types of frontis

IV. 1946 - 1948
   #1 - #18, including first edition #18
   Thin orange-red (or orange-brown) cover
   Small square picture
   #18 (1947) Haunted House cover and eps
      began; wrap spine dj; war paper
   (Reprints have their original dj formats)
   Plain frontis
Variations: various types/colors eps

V. 1948 - 1951
   #1 - #22, including first editions #19 - #22
   Thin red cover
   Haunted House cover and eps
   Wrap spine dj
   (Reprints have the original format djs)
   Plain frontis or no frontis
   #19 paper can be war or good
   #20, #21, #22 good paper
   #21, #22 cover has weave look

VI. 1952 - 1963
   #1 - #34, including first editions #23 - #34
   Thin tweed cover (reddish or brownish)
   Haunted House cover
   Wrap spine dj
   (Reprints of #1 - #8 have new wrap djs; the
      others are original djs)
   #23 - #32 Haunted House eps
   #26 - #34 multiple line drawings
   #33 - #34 two children w/girl eps
   Good paper
   Plain frontis

VII. 1963 - 1967
   #1 (two versions) - #38, including first editions
      #35 - #38, except #30, #31, #33*
   Green spine picture cover
   Haunted House eps and two children w/girl
      eps
   #35, #36, #37 and #38 (1964 - 1967) are in PC
      only
   Two children w/ girl eps.

* Volumes 30, 31, and 33 do not exist in the
Picture Cover format.

## Tempo (Grosset & Dunlap)

VIII. 1967 - 1968
   #1 - #4
   Paperback
   Revised texts
   Photo cover
   No inside pictures

## Reprints

Type 1.
   1976 to present by Ameron Books
   Most editions available
   Tall library bindings
   Photocopy djs

Type 2.
   1994 by Applewood Books
   #1 - #2
   Now out of print
   These are similar to the original books of
      Format I. *The Haunted Attic* (#2) is not the
      first edition printing with Judy's birthday
      cited on page 160.

## Foreign Editions

### Denmark
Judy Bolton-Bøgerne, Published by Spektrum

Skyggen Der Forsvandt (*The Vanishing Shadow*, 1970)
Mysteriet På Loffet (*The Haunted Attic*, 1970)
Klokkespillet (*The Invisible Chimes*, 1971)
Syv Dages Mystik (*Seven Strange Clues*, 1971)

### Sweden
Betty, published by B. Wahlstroms Flickbocker

Betty och spöket pa vinden (*The Haunted Attic*, 1970s)
Betty och den gulsa valnaden (*The Yellow Phantom*, 1973)
Betty och det gömda rummet (*The Secret of the Barred Window*, 1977)
Betty och den kidnappade flickan (*The Secret of the Musical Tree*, 1970s)
(Other Swedish editions may exist.)

### Norway
Judy Bolton-Mysteriene av Margaret Sutton, published by N.W. Damm and Son, Oslo

Fantomskyggen (*The Vanishing Shadow*, 1952)
Det Spoker Pa Loffet (*The Haunted Attic*, 1952)
Den Gatefulle Melodien (*The Invisible Chimes*, 1952)
Hva Kjelleren Gjemte (*Seven Strange Clues*, 1952)
De Levende Masken (*The Ghost Parade*, 1952)
Den Gule Kjolen (*The Yellow Phantom*, 1953)
Den Magiske Kule (*The Mystic Ball*, 1953)
Stemmen I Kofferten (*The Voice in the Suitcase*, 1953)
Den Halve Katten (*The Mysterious Half Cat*, 1953)

### Iceland
Júdy Bolton series, published by Bókaútgáfan Nordiá

Júdy Bolton (*The Vanishing Shadow*, 1949)
Júdy Bolton, í Kvennaskóla (*The Haunted Attic*, 1950)
Júdy Bolton, Eignast Nyja Vinkonu (*The Invisible Chimes*, 1951)

### Spain
Judy Bolton y Cía, published by Ediciones Tooray, S.A.

La Sombra Fugitiva (*The Vanishing Shadow*, 1970s)
El Atico Misterioso (*The Haunted Attic*, 1970s)
Las Campanas Invisibles (*The Invisible Chimes*, 1972)
Siete Extrañas Pistas (*Seven Strange Clues*, 1972)
El Desfile de los Fantasmas (*The Ghost Parade*, 1970s)
El Espectro Amarillo (*The Yellow Phantom*, 1970s)
La Bola Misteriosa (*The Mystic Ball*)
Una Voz en la Maleta (*The Voice in the Suitcase*)
El Misterioso Medio Gato (*The Mysterious Half Cat*)

Note: The translation of the Spanish series is "Judy Bolton and Company," and it was described as "the adventures of a group of boys and girls," and was meant to appeal to both boys and girls.

## 1. The Vanishing Shadow

1932 Edition. 218 Pages.

Judy discovers that the construction of the Roulsville Dam may cause it to burst and her brother, Horace, warns the townspeople before it happens. The town is lost, all are saved and Horace becomes a hero.

Note: "Illustrated by Pelagie Doane" does not appear on the front of the first dust jacket, as it does on all the others from *The Haunted Attic* through *The Secret of the Musical Tree*.

1964 Edition. 172 Pages.

Many details, such as the disappearance of Blackberry during the flood, are changed.

1967 Edition. 157 Pages.

The plot is revised again. This time Judy is not kidnapped.

Dust Jacket A. - 1932 - 1951
Illustrator: Pelagie Doane
Format I.      $5.00-$75.00
Format II.     $5.00-$50.00
Format III.    $4.00-$35.00
Format IV.     $4.00-$25.00
Format V.      $2.00-$20.00

Dust Jacket B. - 1952 - 1963
Illustrator: ?
Format VI.     $2.00-$25.00

Picture Cover A. - 1963
(Same as Dust Jacket B)
Format VII.    $5.00-$25.00

Picture Cover B. - 1964 - 1967
Revised text
Illustrator: ?
Format VII.    $5.00-$15.00

Paperback - 1967 - 1968
Second revised text
Photographic cover
Format VIII.   $2.00-$30.00

# 1. The Vanishing Shadow

**1.** DJ A.

**1.** DJ B/PC A.

**1.** PC B.

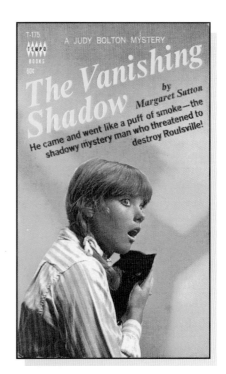

**1.** PB.

**2.** DJ A.

**2.** DJ B/PC A.

## 2. The Haunted Attic

1932 Edition. 212 Pages.

Judy solves the mystery of the ghost in the attic of
the new family home in Farringdon. The mystery of
Peter's birth is also solved. Of special note is that
on page 160 of the first printing of the book, the
party invitation is for Halloween and Judy's birthday. In all other printings, the reference to Judy's
birthday is omitted.

Note: On the front and spine of the first dust jacket
it reads "By Margaret Sutton," the only book in the
series to have the "by" added.

1967 Edition. 155 Pages.

The plot is revised, shortened and modernized.

Note: In all formats, except for the first printing,
*The Haunted Attic* seems to be the easiest to find of
all Judy Bolton books.

> Dust Jacket A. - 1932 - 1953
> Illustrator: Pelagie Doane
> Format I.          $5.00-$100.00
> (First Edition with birthday, page 160)
> Format I.          $5.00-$50.00
> Judy's birthday not cited
> Format II.         $5.00-$40.00
> Format III.        $4.00-$30.00
> Format IV.         $4.00-$20.00
> Format V.          $2.00-$15.00

**2.** PB

> Dust Jacket B. - 1954 - 1963
> Illustrator: ?
> Format VI.         $2.00-$12.00
>
> Picture Cover A. - 1964 - 1967
> (Same as Dust Jacket B)
> Format VII.        $5.00-$12.00
>
> Paperback - 1967 - 1968
> Revised text
> Photographic cover
> Format VIII.       $3.00-$30.00

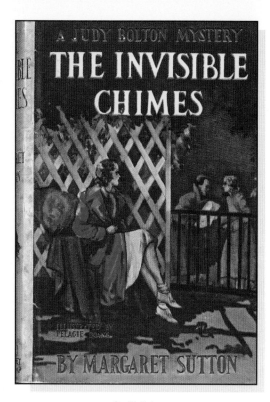

**3.** DJ A.

# 3. The Invisible Chimes

1932 Edition. 213 Pages.

Judy befriends Honey, who claimed to have amnesia after a robbery, solves the mystery of her identity and helps her rejoin her family.

1968 Edition. 154 Pages.

A revised and shortened edition for the paperback version.

> Dust Jacket A. - 1932 - 1952
> Illustrator: Pelagie Doane
> Format I.          $5.00-$75.00
> Format II.         $5.00-$50.00
> Format III.        $4.00-$35.00
> Format IV.         $4.00-$25.00
> Format V.          $2.00-$20.00
>
> Dust Jacket B. - 1953 - 1963
> Illustrator: ?
> Format VI.         $2.00-$25.00
>
> Picture Cover A. - 1964 - 1967
> (Same as Dust Jacket B)
> Format VII.        $5.00-$20.00
>
> Paperback - 1967 - 1968
> Revised text
> Photographic cover
> Format VII.        $5.00-$30.00

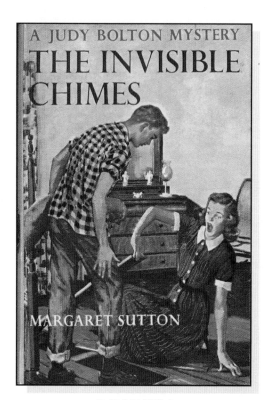

**3.** DJ B/PC A.

**3.** PB

**4.** DJ A.

**4.** DJ B/PC A.

## 4. Seven Strange Clues

1932 Edition. 210 Pages.

The Bolton's cellar is haunted, Farringdon Girls' High burns down, and the two events are related and tied to the Vincent family.

1968 Edition. 156 Pages.

A revised and shortened version for the last new Grosset & Dunlap (Tempo) Judy Bolton format.

      Dust Jacket A. - 1932 - 1950
      Illustrator: Pelagie Doane
      Format I.         $5.00-$75.00
      Format II.        $5.00-$50.00
      Format III.      $4.00-$35.00
      Format IV.      $4.00-$25.00
      Format V.       $2.00-$20.00

      Dust Jacket B. - 1951 - 1963
      Illustrator: ?
      Format VI.      $2.00-$25.00

      Picture Cover A. - 1964 - 1967
      (Same as Dust Jacket B)
      Format VII.    $5.00-$40.00

      Paperback - 1968
      Revised text
      Photographic cover
      Format VIII.   $7.00-$40.00

**4.** PB.

## 5. The Ghost Parade

1933. 217 Pages

Judy purchases some Indian masks on the way to the Thousand Islands. These masks cause trouble at a camp there and Blackberry saves Judy from villain Slippery McQuirk.

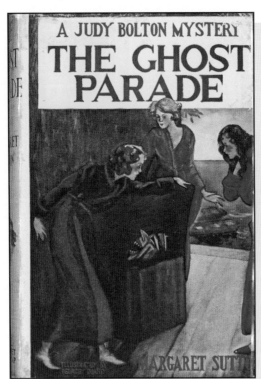

**5.** DJ A.

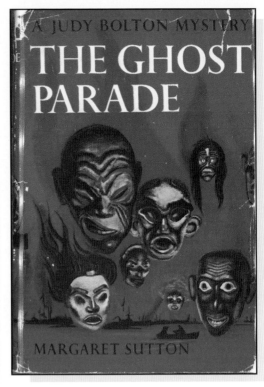

**5.** DJ B/PC A.

Dust Jacket A. - 1933 - 1951
Illustrator: Pelagie Doane
Format I.     $5.00-$75.00
Format II.    $5.00-$50.00
Format III.   $5.00-$35.00
Format IV.    $5.00-$25.00
Format V.     $2.00-$25.00

Dust Jacket B. - 1952 - 1963
Illustrator: ?
Format VI.   $2.00-$25.00

Picture Cover A. - 1964 - 1967
(Same as Dust Jacket B)
Format VII.  $5.00-$20.00

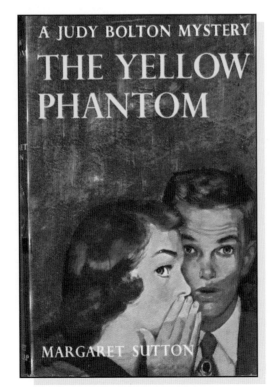

**6.** DJ B/PC A.

**6.** DJ A.

## 6. The Yellow Phantom

1933. 210 Pages.

Judy and Irene go New York to visit Pauline Faulkner. Irene falls in love with mystery writer Dale Meredith. Judy works for Pauline's employer, literary agent Emily Grimshaw, and through her solves a mystery involving Irene's past.

    Dust Jacket A. - 1933 - 1950
    Illustrator: Pelagie Doane
    Format I.      $5.00-$75.00
    Format II.     $5.00-$50.00
    Format III.    $4.00-$35.00
    Format IV.     $4.00-$25.00
    Format V.      $2.00-$20.00

    Dust Jacket B. - 1951 - 1963
    Illustrator: ?
    Format VI.     $2.00-$25.00

    Picture Cover A. - 1964 - 1967
    (Same as Dust Jacket B)
    Format VII.    $5.00-$20.00

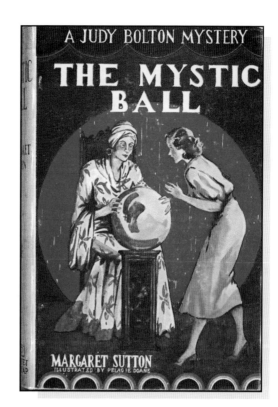

**7.** DJ A.

## 7. The Mystic Ball

1934. 212 Pages.

Judy exposes crystal gazer Madame Wanda's trickery to save Irene's engagement to Dale.

    Dust Jacket A. - 1934 - 1953
    Illustrator: Pelagie Doane
    Format I.      $5.00-$75.00
    Format II.     $5.00-$50.00
    Format III.    $4.00-$35.00
    Format IV.     $3.00-$30.00
    Format V.      $2.00-$25.00
    Format VI.     $2.00-$25.00

    Dust Jacket B. - 1954 - 1963
    Illustrator: ?
    Format VI.     $2.00-$25.00

    Picture Cover A. - 1964 - 1967
    (Same as Dust Jacket B)
    Format VII.    $5.00-$20.00

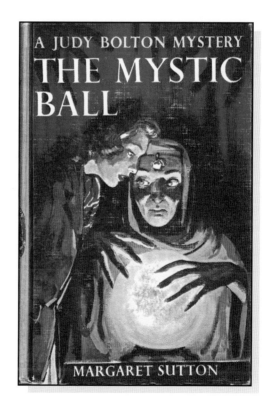

**7.** DJ B/PC A.

**8.** DJ A.

## 8. The Voice in the Suitcase

1935. 215 Pages.

Judy and Honey discover a man lying face-down in a ditch near a suitcase from which a cry is heard. These mysteries are solved at the Golden Wedding party of Grandma and Grandpa Brady.

    Dust Jacket A. - 1935 - 1951
    Illustrator: Pelagie Doane
    Format I.       $5.00-$75.00
    Format II.     $5.00-$50.00
    Format III.    $4.00-$35.00
    Format IV.    $3.00-$30.00
    Format V.     $3.00-$25.00

    Dust Jacket B. - 1952 - 1963
    Illustrator: ?
    Format VI.    $2.00-$25.00

    Picture Cover A. - 1963 - 1967
    (Same as Dust Jacket B)
    Format VI.    $5.00-$20.00

**8.** DJ B/PC A.

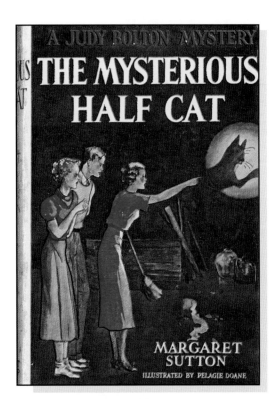

**9.** DJ A/PC A.

# 9. The Mysterious Half Cat

1936. 215 Pages.

More mysteries in cellars: at the Chinese laundry in downtown Farringdon and on Upper Grove Street, where "scrub women and worse" live. Both involve Dora Scott, her little sister, Carol, and their missing father.

    Dust Jacket A. - 1936 - 1963
    Illustrator: Pelagie Doane
    Format I.      $5.00-$75.00
    Format II.     $5.00-$50.00
    Format III.    $4.00-$35.00
    Format IV.    $4.00-$30.00
    Format V.     $2.00-$25.00
    Format VI.    $2.00-$25.00

    Picture Cover A. - 1963 - 1967
    (Same as Dust Jacket A)
    Format VII.    $5.00-$20.00

# 10. The Riddle of the Double Ring

1937. 216 Pages.

Judy becomes secretly engaged to Arthur. While he is in the hospital with an injury suffered in the crash of his plane, Judy searches for Lorraine, who is in love with him. Lorraine, in an attempt to be like Judy, was pursuing fur thieves.

    Dust Jacket A. - 1937 - 1963
    Illustrator: Pelagie Doane
    Format I.      $5.00-$75.00
    Format II.     $5.00-$50.00
    Format III.    $4.00-$35.00
    Format IV.    $4.00-$30.00
    Format V.     $2.00-$25.00
    Format VI.    $2.00-$25.00

    Picture Cover A. - 1964 - 1967
    (Same as Dust Jacket A)
    Format VII.    $5.00-$20.00

# 11. The Unfinished House

1938. 250 Pages.

A housing developer attempts to frighten Mrs. Piper and her son, Algie, away from Roulsville where they are building a house designed by Arthur Farringdon-Pett on a 15-foot-wide lot they won. The sounds of horses and blood on the snow is used to intimidate them because they will not purchase an adjacent property at an inflated price.

    Dust Jacket A. - 1938 - 1963
    Illustrator: Pelagie Doane
    Format II.     $5.00-$50.00
    Format III.    $4.00-$35.00
    Format IV.    $4.00-$30.00
    Format V.     $2.00-$25.00
    Format VI.    $2.00-$25.00

**10.** DJ A/PC A.

**11.** DJ A/PC A.

Picture Cover A. - 1963 - 1967
(Same as Dust Jacket A)
Format VII.    $6.00-$25.00

## 12. The Midnight Visitor

1939. 249 Pages.

More problems from the Vincent family: Judy and Peter find Sally in a closed-up house that is a twin to the Bolton home. A strange man comes to the Bolton door at midnight and then disappears. All this is related to a curious last will and testament.

Dust Jacket A. - 1939 - 1963
Illustrator: Pelagie Doane
Format II.  $5.00-$50.00
Format III.  $4.00-$35.00
Format IV.  $4.00-$30.00
Format V.  $2.00-$25.00
Format VI.  $2.00-$25.00

Picture Cover A. - 1965 - 1967
(Same as Dust Jacket A)
Format VII.  $12.00-$35.00

**12.** DJ A/PC A.

**13.** DJ A/PC A.

## 13. The Name on the Bracelet

1940. 216 Pages.

Judy and Peter become engaged. When Judy goes to New York to meet her namesake, Irene's new baby, she loses the diamond from her ring. She discovers that Irene's baby had been switched in the hospital and Irene's husband, Dale, does not want Irene to know it.

Dust Jacket A. - 1940 - 1963
Illustrator: Pelagie Doane
Format II.  $5.00-$50.00
Format III.  $4.00-$35.00
Format IV.  $4.00-$30.00
Format V.  $2.00-$25.00
Format VI.  $2.00-$25.00

Picture Cover A. - 1963 - 1967
(Same as Dust Jacket A)
Format VII.  $6.00-$25.00

## 14. The Clue in the Patchwork Quilt

1941. 214 Pages.

Linda Leonard, who was once engaged to Judy's Uncle John, comes home for Grandma Smeed's funeral. She and Judy solve another family secret that pertains to a marriage that was not approved and discover Judy's almost exact look-alike cousin, Roxy, using clues found in Grandma's quilt. Judy inherits the Smeed farm at Dry Brook Hollow.

Note: This book includes one of the very few instances in the Judy Bolton series where something establishes a time period: "[Linda] would have been our aunt if Uncle John hadn't been killed in the last war. That was over twenty years ago..." (Page 2) "She was only sixteen then...She was still beautiful at thirty-eight...twenty years separated them." (Page 20) This means that Linda was born in about 1902 and Judy in about 1922, based on this book, which, of course, does not match with the dates of the earlier books in the series.

Dust Jacket A. - 1941 - 1963
Illustrator: Pelagie Doane
Format II. $5.00-$50.00
Format III. $4.00-$35.00
Format IV. $4.00-$30.00
Format V. $2.00-$25.00
Format VI. $2.00-$25.00

Picture Cover A. - 1965 - 1967
(Same as Dust Jacket A)
Format VII.  $12.00-$35.00

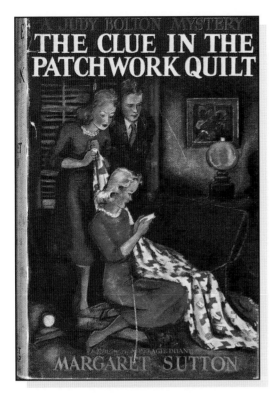

**14.** DJ A/PC A.

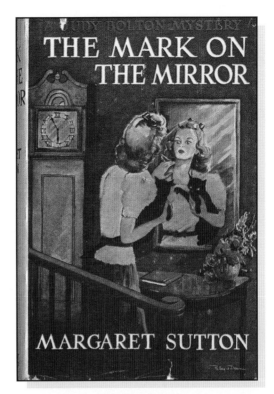

**15.** DJ A/PC A.

## 15. The Mark on the Mirror

1942. 206 Pages.

A masked messenger delivers a mirror to Judy at
her bridal shower. Peter is involved in a child cus-
tody case for an adopted girl who is later reunited
with her family. Will Horace lose Honey to Forrest?

> Dust Jacket A. - 1942 - 1963
> Illustrator: Pelagie Doane
> Format II.　　$5.00-$50.00
> Format III.　　$4.00-$35.00
> Format IV.　　$4.00-$30.00
> Format V.　　$2.00-$25.00
> Format VI.　　$2.00-$25.00

## 16. The Secret of the Barred Window

1943. 207 Pages.

Judy goes to New York to buy a wedding dress,
which she loses in Connecticut when she goes
there with Pauline to search for the missing author
Alice Bradley, Emily Grimshaw's client from *The
Yellow Phantom.* Ten-year-old Roberta Dunn, who
is involved in all this, lives next door to the house
with the barred window, Miss Bradley's home
before she lost her memory.

Note: This is the last dust jacket to have a white
spine with the small Judy Bolton head symbol on
it.

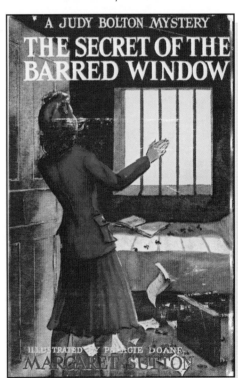

**16.** DJ A/PC A.

Dust Jacket A. - 1943 - 1963
| | |
|---|---|
| Format III. | $4.00-$35.00 |
| Format IV. | $4.00-$30.00 |
| Format V. | $2.00-$25.00 |
| Format VI. | $2.00-$25.00 |

Picture Cover A. - 1964 - 1967
(Same as Dust Jacket A)
| | |
|---|---|
| Format VII. | $10.00-$30.00 |

**17.** DJ A/PC A.

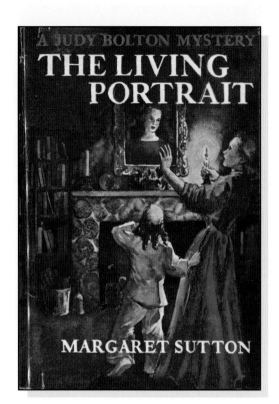

**18.** DJ A/PC A.

# 17. The Rainbow Riddle

1946. 200 Pages.

Roberta shows up unexpectedly at Judy's and Peter's wedding and begs them not to open the present from Irene and Dale. At the reception, she is seen running off to the woods. A terrible explosion follows. On their honeymoon, Judy helps Peter solve the riddle of the Rainbow Ring. Roberta's prayers are answered: She leaves the Griggs home to live with Judy and Peter. Peter leaves to begin training as a G-man.

Note: This is the first wrap-around-the-spine dust jacket. The symbol picture of Judy is larger than on the white spine dust jackets.

    Dust Jacket A. - 1946 - 1963
    Illustrator: Pelagie Doane
    Format III.    $4.00-$35.00
    Format IV.    $4.00-$30.00
    Format V.    $2.00-$25.00
    Format VI.    $2.00-$25.00

    Picture Cover A. - 1964 - 1967
    (Same as Dust Jacket A)
    Format VII.    $10.00-$30.00

# 18. The Living Portrait

1947. 208 Pages.

Peter, now an FBI agent, sets up an office in his and Judy's home in Dry Brook Hollow, from where he tries to trace a fortune in stolen cash. A portrait that Judy bought at an auction causes confusion when Roberta says it is her teacher. The portrait changes its appearance.

Note: There in no spine symbol (picture of Judy) on the wrap dust jacket.

    Dust Jacket A. - 1947 - 1963
    Format IV.    $4.00-$30.00
    Format V.    $2.00-$30.00
    Format VI.    $2.00-$25.00

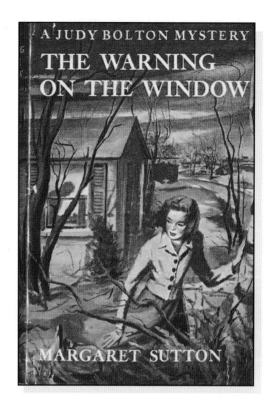

**19.** DJ A/PC A.

**20.** DJ A/PC A.

# 19. The Secret of the Musical Tree

1948. 216 Pages.

The Junior FBI (Roberta and two friends) helps Judy solve the puzzle included in Roxy's Christmas present, which was opened early. Judy takes Roxy's place in Cleveland to bring the criminals who have taken over the Zoller home to justice. Will Judy and her family be together for Christmas?

Note: This is the last Pelagie Doane dust jacket. The spine symbol of Judy on the wrap dust jacket is a new one, the head view from *The Rainbow Riddle*.

> Dust Jacket A. - 1948 - 1963
> Illustrator: Pelagie Doane
> Format V.      $4.00-$35.00
> Format VI.     $4.00-$30.00
>
> Picture Cover A. - 1963 - 1967
> (Same as Dust Jacket A)
> Format VII.    $10.00-$30.00

# 20. The Warning on the Window

1949. 211 Pages.

Once again the rebuilding of Roulsville is thwarted. Peter is attacked, resulting in a coma. Judy places her life in jeopardy finding out why.

Note: This volume carries another new spine symbol picture of Judy. It is used until the end of the series. Beginning with the next volume, *The Clue of the Stone Lantern*, Judy's portrait is superimposed over a dark oval, that later has various sizes of black banners under it with the volume number listed. From *The Warning on the Window* until the end of the series, it appears that each dust jacket or picture cover and all the interior pictures in the books are done by different artists and the only artist's signature is on the cover of *The Warning on the Window*.

> Dust Jacket A. - 1949 - 1963
> Illustrator: Grossi (?)
> Format V.      $4.00-$35.00
> Format VI.     $4.00-$30.00
>
> Picture Cover A. - 1963 - 1967
> (Same as Dust Jacket A)
> Format VII.    $10.00-$30.00

**21.** DJ A/PC A.

**22.** DJ A/PC A.

**23.** DJ A/PC A.

## 21. The Clue of the Stone Lantern

1950. 210 Pages.

Roberta begins to remember things from her past and it is discovered that she had been kidnapped years earlier. She returns home.

Note: This story and the following one, *The Spirit of Fog Island*, are without a doubt the apogee of Margaret Sutton's Judy Bolton mysteries and her writing career. After that point, the books decline in quality, but some of the fault could be that Grosset & Dunlap now wanted them aimed at younger readers, although the dust jackets still carried the code "100-150," which means that the books were intended for ten- to fifteen-year-olds.

Dust Jacket A. - 1950 - 1963
Format V.        $4.00-$35.00
Format VI.       $4.00-$30.00

Picture Cover A. - 1965 - 1967
(Same as Dust Jacket A)
Format VII.    $12.00-$35.00

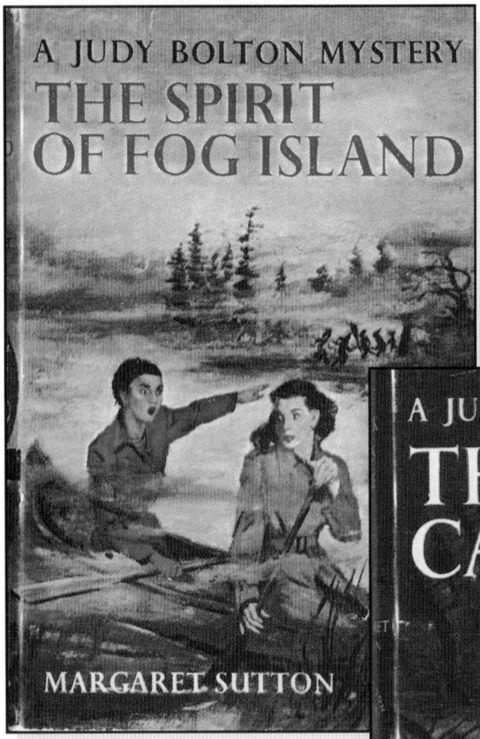

## 22. The Spirit of Fog Island

1951. 210 Pages.

In the first Judy Bolton Mystery to take place entirely outside Pennsylvania, Judy travels from Chicago to an Indian reservation in northern Wisconsin because of a mistaken identity. She becomes friends with Nona Cloud, an Indian girl, and helps her protect ancestral lands.

Dust Jacket A. - 1951 - 1963
Format V.        $4.00-$35.00
Format VI.       $4.00-$30.00

Picture Cover A. - 1964 - 1967
(Same as Dust Jacket A)
Format VII.    $10.00-$30.00

## 23. The Black Cat's Clue

1952. 210 Pages.

Judy becomes friends with her neighbor, Holly Potter, and her family and is involved in the problems with David Potter's will. There are also mysterious apparitions in Judy's garden. (This is Blackberry's fourth cover appearance.)

Dust Jacket A. - 1952 - 1963
Format VI.      $4.00-$35.00

Picture Cover A. - 1964 - 1967
(Same as Dust Jacket A)
Format VII.    $10.00-$30.00

## 24. The Forbidden Chest

1953. 210 Pages.

Judy and Holly discover that a valuable paper-weight is missing after a visit from young Harold Wilcox. Judy solves his problems after following him on a train bound for California.

Note: This is the last Judy Bolton mystery to have more than 200 pages. Unlike the Nancy Drew books that were reduced to twenty chapters, the Judy Bolton books continued to have twenty-four or twenty-five chapters but they were all considerably shortened, although this book has only twenty-seven lines per page and the next has thirty-three, which would change the page count somewhat. (*The Unfinished House* of 1938, the longest book of the series at 250 pages, has twenty-seven lines of text per page.)

> Dust Jacket A. - 1953 - 1963
> Format VI.     $4.00-$35.00
>
> Picture cover A. - 1965 - 1967
> (Same as dust Jacket A)
> Format VII.     $10.00-$35.00

**24.** DJ A/PC A.

## 25. The Haunted Road

1954. 181 Pages.

Judy investigates strange doings on a road where there are problems with truck theft.

> Dust Jacket A. - 1954 - 1963
> Format VI.     $4.00-$40.00
>
> Picture Cover A. - 1964 - 1967
> (Same as Dust Jacket A)
> Format VII.     $10.00-$35.00

**25.** DJ A/PC A.

## 26. The Clue in the Ruined Castle

1955. 176 Pages.

The one-hundred-year-old owner of a castle is missing a large sum of money.

Note: There are twenty-eight lines of text per page.

> Dust Jacket A. - 1955 - 1963
> Format VI.     $4.00-$40.00
>
> Picture Cover A. - 1963 - 1967
> (Same as Dust Jacket A)
> Format VII.     $10.00-$35.00

**26.** DJ A/PC A.

## 27. The Trail of the Green Doll

1956. 180 Pages.

Judy takes in boarders because Peter's job with the FBI keeps him away from home too much. Helen Riker and her two children act strangely about a doll.

Note: There are only twenty-five lines of text per page.

Dust Jacket A. - 1956 - 1963
Format VI.     $4.00-$40.00

Picture Cover A. - 1963(?) - 1976
(Same as Dust Jacket A)
Format VII.     $10.00-$35.00

**27.** DJ A/PC A.

## 28. The Haunted Fountain

1957. 180 Pages.

Judy and Horace investigate a huge outdoor fountain on the Brandt Estate that Judy had heard speak when she was fourteen. They help an injured man whom they find in a room under the fountain.

Note: There are twenty-eight lines of text per page.

Dust Jacket A. - 1957 - 1963
Format VI.     $6.00-$50.00

Picture Cover A. - 1965 - 1967
(Same as Dust Jacket A)
Format VII.     $10.00-$40.00

**28.** DJ A/PC A.

## 29. The Clue of the Broken Wing

1958. 182 Pages.

In a plot filled with coincidences, Judy finds the broken [off] wing of an angel statute as she and Peter are leaving Dry Brook Hollow to spend Christmas with Dale and Irene in the Parkville section of Brooklyn. When they get there, she discovers that Irene's and Dale's house is gone and that the little girl of the neighbors across the street has been missing for a year. Guess where in Pennsylvania the child has been all the while?

Dust Jacket A. - 1958 - 1963
Format VI.     $10.00-$60.00

Picture Cover A. - 1963 - 1967
(Same as Dust Jacket A)
Format VII.     $15.00-$45.00

**29.** DJ A/PC A.

## 30. The Phantom Friend

1959. 174 Pages.

Judy, Flo and Pauline pretend that an empty seat in a New York restaurant is occupied by a "phantom." A girl who claims to be an actual phantom takes the seat. The effect of subliminal television advertising is also explored.

> Dust Jacket A. - 1959 - 1963 (?)
> Format VI.    $25.00-$70.00+

Note: There was no picture cover printing of this book.

## 31. The Discovery at the Dragon's Mouth

1960. 182 Pages.

In another case of mistaken identity, Judy receives a package and is instructed by the giver to "meet me at the Dragon's Mouth." Judy and Honey drive from Pennsylvania to Yellowstone Park when they discover this is where the Dragon's Mouth, a hot spring, is located.

> Dust Jacket A. - 1960 - 1963 (?)
> Format VI.    $25.00-$70.00+

Note: There was not picture cover printing of this book.

## 32. The Whispered Watchword

1961. 180 Pages.

Judy and Peter visit Washington, D.C., Blackberry turns up missing and a statue of Roger Williams in the Capitol's Statuary Hall seems to whisper a strange message. Senator Hockett is involved in all this.

Note: Judy Bolton, like Nancy Drew, solved mysteries of whispers and voices from unknown sources many times.

> Dust Jacket A. - 1961 - 1963
> Format VI.    $20.00-$80.00
>
> Picture Cover A. - 1963 - 1967
> (Same as Dust Jacket A)
> Format VII.    $20.00-$60.00

**30.** DJ A.

**31.** DJ A.

**32.** DJ A/PC A.

89

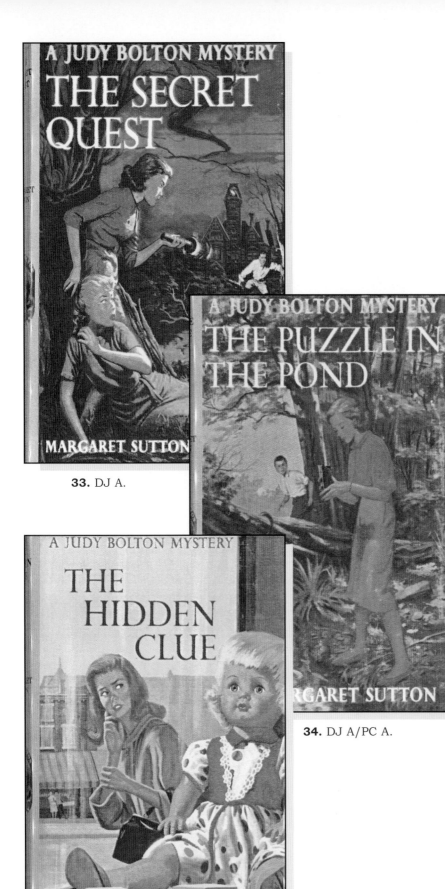

**33.** DJ A.

**34.** DJ A/PC A.

**35.** PC A.

## 33. The Secret Quest

1962. 174 Pages.

Peter's sister, Honey, picks up the wrong suitcase at the Washington Airport when she comes to join Peter and Judy and later sees others wearing her clothing. This mystery also deals with Sutton's view on poltergeists.

> Dust Jacket A. - 1962 - 1963 (?)
> Format VI.    $25-$85.00

Note: There is no picture cover format of this book.

## 34. The Puzzle in the Pond

1963. 170 Pages.

The Roulsville Flood of the first Judy Bolton Mystery is the basis for the plot again. Judy traces the looters of family furniture that is turning up six years after the flood.

> Dust Jacket A. - 1963
> Format VI.    $20.00-$85.00

> Picture Cover A. - 1966 - 1967
> (Same as Dust Jacket A)
> Format VII.    $25.00-$75.00

Note: This is the last Judy Bolton Mystery printed with a dust jacket.

## 35. The Hidden Clue

1964. 167 Pages.

Judy takes in a little boy and his sister who were displaced by a fire at an orphanage and searches for their parents, another familiar Judy Bolton Mystery theme.

> Picture Cover A. - 1964 - 1967
> Format VII.    $25.00-$100.00

## 36. The Pledge of the Twin Knights

1965. 172 Pages.

Judy finds a warning about her "curiosity" inside a chess game piece but this does not deter her from investigating a prison break and the last of many, many intruders in her home.

> Picture Cover A. - 1965 - 1967
> Format VII.    $25.00-$125.00

## 37. The Search for the Glowing Hand

1966. 172 Pages.

Judy and Peter attempt to aid Muslims who are being discriminated against and threatened. (Margaret Sutton attempts social commentary.)

> Picture Cover A. - 1966 - 1967
> Format VII.    $25.00-$150.00

## 38. The Secret of the Sand Castle

1967. 174 Pages.

Judy takes a bus to New York, where she is joined by Irene and little Judy, Flo, and Pauline, and they all go to a cottage named The Sand Castle on Fire Island. This cottage is in dispute in an estate claimed by many people, including Judy's cousin, Roxy, and may be the site of buried treasure.

Note: Although better written and plotted than many of the later Judy Bolton Mystery stories, this one contains many familiar elements of Margaret Sutton's books, such as estranged relatives brought together by a death in the family. This was the last Judy Bolton book printed by Grosset & Dunlap, although page 174 states that "THE STRANGE LIKENESS would plunge her into her next mystery." On the last page of the book, Judy mentions her horse, Ginger, and thinks of her cat, Blackberry, back home in Dry Brook Hollow, right where *The Vanishing Shadow* began thirty-five years earlier.

> Picture Cover A. - 1967
> Format VII.    $35.00-$225.00

**36.** PC A.

**37.** PC A.

**38.** PC A.

# CHAPTER 5

# The Beverly Gray Mystery Series

The Beverly Gray Series has assumed cult status. There is brisk trading of the twenty-six different titles everywhere used books are sold, including eBay on the Internet. There is a bi-monthly magazine, *Susabella Passengers and Friends*, for collectors and fans of Beverly Gray, although this newsletter also addresses other series books.

One person—Clair Blank—not a committee, wrote the Beverly Gray stories, so they have a uniform style and theme. This series began as adventure/mysteries in a college setting, which was a popular theme for girls' series books in the early 20th century. A similarly themed series was the "Betty Wales" books of 1904 to 1917. The first four volumes of this set even have the same type of titles, for example, *Betty Wells, Freshman*. At the time Clair Blank began the Beverly Gray books, college life for women was still considered a rather exotic adventure. The liberated life continued when Beverly graduated from Vernon College and went to New York City, where she shared an apartment with other young women seeking a career and an independent existence apart from the traditional family. Beverly also had boyfriends and traveled around the country and around the world with them, but they were always chaperoned or in the company of others in an intimate setting or situation.

From Volume 1, both by A.L. Burt and Grosset & Dunlap, through Volume 16, the series was called "The Beverly Gray College Mystery Series," although Beverly's association with college ended with Volume 4, *Beverly Gray, Senior*. Beginning with Volume 17, *Beverly Gray's Assignment*, in 1947, the series was called "The Beverly Gray Mystery Series."

Clair Blank never gave a vivid physical description of Beverly. This can make the reader develop his or her own image of what she looks like or it can cause Beverly to have a less individual identity than other girl sleuths and heroines. I never formed an exact picture of what she looked like, as I did for other "girl sleuths," such as Nancy Drew or Judy Bolton. The fact that the series had so many different styles of dust jackets and frontispieces also hurt the image of Beverly, as she looked entirely different on various dust jacket presentations.

Another factor that is bothersome when I read the Beverly Gray series is that she has too many close friends. I did not recognize a clear distinction between the personalities of the three most important friends, Lois, Lenora and Shirley, although each had different goals and interests. I could not tell the guys apart clearly or remember exactly who was whose boyfriend, as there was an uneven balance of them. When the yacht *Susabella* sailed with all the friends, there were always more men than women aboard or running into them in their ports of call. The villains in these books are not jealous, spiteful types like Kay Vincent in the Judy Bolton series. They are truly evil, like Count Alexis de Franchiny who often tried to have those who did not cooperate with him murdered. Beverly Gray got to visit more exotic locales than any other series character of the 1930s and 1940s and she became acquainted with many exotic foreigners. The best example of this is the cannibals on the South Seas island in *Beverly Gray's Treasure Hunt*. The plots and situations of the Beverly Gray books involve more fantasy and imagination than those of other authors and it would be more difficult for readers to identify with the characters in the books on a personal level. Nancy Drew was one of the most daring of all the girl sleuths but even she never crept into the Taj Mahal in the middle of the night or viewed a typhoon from the deck of a yacht in the Pacific Ocean and got washed overboard as a result. Most Beverly Gray books concentrate on adventure and romance more than in solving a specific mystery or interrelated mysteries.

A good example of the rather odd construction of a typical Beverly Gray "Mystery" is found in the second book of the series, *Beverly Gray, Sophomore*. The first twenty chapters of the book concentrate on the mystery of drug smugglers at the Horler mansion and this mystery is totally resolved. Then there are three chapters in which Beverly and Larry disappear in his plane. This mystery is concluded. The last four chapters of the book are about the mystery of who stole the history exams at Vernon College. Neither of the two smaller mysteries had anything to do with the main mystery or with each other. It would have seemed more logical to have tied the two smaller mysteries into the larger one, or at least to have run them concurrently with the main problem to be solved, rather than have the novel conclude with one large story with two smaller ones tacked onto the end of it.

It is reported that author Clair Blank did not visit the places she described so vividly, such as India, China and Japan, but like Edgar Rice Burroughs who never traveled in Africa but located Tarzan there, she created a setting from reading about it and studying. Naturally there are many stereotypical foreign people in the Beverly Gray books, as in all juvenile literature of the time, but none are too derogatorily portrayed. One mistake is improper naming, such as giving Hindus names that would be more correct for Arabs or Muslims, like Omar el-Hamel (later el Hamel) in *Beverly Gray's Career,* for example.

The Beverly Gray stories are all fast-paced and every book covers many complicated plot elements or at least takes the characters through several different situations and locations, although too many of them have little relation to the main plot or the "mystery" of the book. Every time that Beverly's life is in danger or she is held captive by evildoers, the chapter or chapters have to be read quickly to see if she is rescued or escapes, although all one has to do is check the front of the book for a list of her further adventures to know that she is saved. But that is not how a young person reasons when involved in reading about an exciting situation.

In one sense it is a shame that author Clair Blank did not have the opportunity to marry Beverly off or plan for her future, as the series was canceled so abruptly, but on the other hand, Beverly Gray lives on forever if these issues are not resolved and we can imagine for ourselves how things worked out for her.

A dust jacket and frontispiece picture that show a young woman wearing high heels and a freshly ironed dress while peering over a rocky cliff on a remote Pacific island where cannibals are endangering treasure seekers is certainly an anachronism in today's world, and it probably was when the book was written. In the actual story (*Treasure Hunt*) Clair Blank did not tell how Beverly was groomed and dressed, but these pictures and plot situations became images that had gone out of style even before the series ended. Now we see this as great fun and diversion because it does represent standards of a time that is gone forever.

## Clair Blank

Clair Blank was born in Allentown, Pennsylvania, on August 5, 1915[1]; she died on August 15, 1965. She is most famous for the Beverly Gray (College) Mystery Series, which was published from 1934 to 1955. Her other series of books was The Adventure Girls, a three-volume set in 1936. Clair Blank's books were first published by A.L. Burt. By 1938, Grosset & Dunlap had taken over the Beverly Gray series and the Adventure Girls trilogy was later reprinted by Saalfield in a more economical edition than that produced by Burt. The Adventure Girls was no doubt planned to be a larger series than it was, but it had to have been hurt by its unattractive dust jacket designs. Based on the dates of book publication, Clair Blank was not yet twenty when her work was first in print. She was married and had two sons. Clair Blank died of cancer while still young.

## The Beverly Gray Books

A.L. Burt published the first eight titles of the Beverly Gray College Mysteries between 1934 and 1937. The Burt books were produced with a high degree of quality that compared with those of the company's competitors, Cupples & Leon Co. and Grosset & Dunlap.

The Burt Beverly Gray books have gray cloth-covered covers and well designed dust jackets. These books (and the early ones from Grosset & Dunlap) measure just a shade more than 8 inches high, the same size as Burt's Elsie Dinsmore books of the same era. The early Nancy Drew books from Grosset & Dunlap were 7 5/8 inches high at this time. There was no reason for the books to be taller than normal, as the line count in them was twenty-seven lines to a page. Nancy Drew had twenty-eight lines per page. The Beverly Gray text was also wider on the page than Grosset & Dunlap's books and the early volumes in the series were about 250 pages, which resulted in a much higher word count than comparable books from Grosset & Dunlap at the time. (The first Nancy Drew book was 210 pages; the first Judy Bolton had 218 pages.)

There was only one picture inside the Beverly Gray books, the frontispiece on glossy paper. This was unusual because it was a reduced size but fuller image black-and-white repeat of the full-color dust jacket. The only artist who gets credit for dust jacket or frontispiece art is Russell H. Tandy, whose signature is on pictures of Volumes 14 and 15 in the 1940s with Grosset & Dunlap. The dust jacket art is unusual also in that there is very little consistency

1 *Susabella Passengers and Friends*, July 1994, page 8.

after the eight Burt covers (which were repeated by Grosset & Dunlap). After these designs, Beverly never looked the same twice except for the two Tandy dust jackets. On some covers she looks like a young girl (*Island Mystery*); on others like a mature woman (*Scoop*). Her hair is many different shades and styles. I feel that this lack of a consistent design hurt sales of the books and prevented them from becoming more popular. Some of the later covers (such as *Beverly Gray's Journey*) are not even particularly professional or attractive and depict the protagonist as rather plain. The Burt covers are consistently the best, as they "tell a story," which is important for the juvenile market, but the very best of all is *Beverly Gray's Island Mystery* because it shows the prettiest Beverly and also tells a story that promises intrigue and mystery.

When Grosset & Dunlap took over the series, the books were the same size and format except that most cloth covers were now light green (orange and gray were also used). The only apparent difference is that all references to the A.L. Burt Company were removed. For the spine of the dust jacket, a bar covered the former publisher's name and the new one was printed over it. Although the early dust jackets were very outdated by the 1950s, Grosset & Dunlap never commissioned new ones and continued to use the originals, even though the inside repeat of the dust jacket for a frontispiece was eliminated. When the size of the books was reduced to the same size as all other Grosset & Dunlap series books by the early 1940s, some edges of print on the titles were cut off.

The most unique change from Burt to Grosset & Dunlap was in the elimination of the sixth Burt title, *Beverly Gray at the World's Fair*, referring to the one that took place at the Century of Progress Exposition in Chicago in 1933 to 1934. Supposedly, this is because the title dated the book. This makes Volume 6 of the Burt series very rare because it was only printed for a couple of years. As a consequence, this is one of the few books in collectible juvenile literature in which a book without a dust jacket can command a high price. The missing dust jacket is easily replaced today. A new one can be created on a laser color printer, which is rather economical. The numbering sequence of the books between Volume 6 and Volume 8 in the Grosset & Dunlap set is also changed.

Although Grosset & Dunlap did not include *Beverly Gray at the World's Fair* among its titles, none of the books in the series that mentioned this event were changed to account for it. Both *Beverly Gray on a World Cruise* and *Beverly Gray's Return*, for example, mention it.

Grosset & Dunlap printed all the Beverly Gray books (except for *Beverly Gray at the World's Fair*) until 1954 with a hard cover and a dust jacket. After that time, the reprint rights were sold to McLoughlin Bros. for Clover Books. The Clover books have a shiny picture cover with bonded cellophane over it that repeats the dust jacket picture on the front and the blue tweed binding of the last of the Grosset & Dunlap books on the back. Clover Books only printed the Grosset & Dunlap titles from Volume 18 (*Beverly Gray's Mystery*) to Volume 25 (*Beverly Gray's Surprise*). This last one was never printed by Grosset & Dunlap although the Judy Bolton book, *The Clue of the Ruined Castle* of 1955, has an advertisement for the Beverly Gray books on the back end flap and lists it. It is not known if *Beverly Gray's Surprise*, available in a picture cover only, is a rare book. It does not seem difficult to locate at a reasonable price.

I can remember the Beverly Gray books in stores during the 1950s, but they were not carried by all the sources that had Grosset & Dunlap books and they were never shelved in abundance, even during the Christmas season, like the Judy Bolton, Nancy Drew and Hardy Boys books were. I would list them third in desirability of all girls' series books, after Nancy Drew and Judy Bolton.

# BEVERLY GRAY BOOK FORMATS

## A. A.L. Burt

I.  1934 - 1937
    #1 - #8, including first editions #1 - #8
    Tall, thick, light gray or red cloth cover
    Blue eps with "house" scene
    Glossy frontis
    Good paper

    1. *Beverly Gray, Freshman* (1934)
    2. *Beverly Gray, Sophomore* (1934)
    3. *Beverly Gray, Junior* (1934)
    4. *Beverly Gray, Senior* (1934)
    5. *Beverly Gray's Career* (1935)
    6. *Beverly Gray at the World's Fair* (1935)
    7. *Beverly Gray on a World Cruise* (1936)
    8. *Beverly Gray in the Orient* (1937)

## B. Grosset & Dunlap

II.  1938 - 1942
     #1 - #12, including first editions #9 - #12
     (Grosset & Dunlap eliminates Burt #6)
     Tall, thick, light green or orange cloth cover
     Dark or light blue eps with "house" scene
     Glossy frontis
     Good paper

III. 1943 - 1948
     #1 - #18, including first editions #13 - #18
     Regular size with smooth cover
     Dark green; dark blue; dark blue w/cameo on
       cover (begins 1946?)
     "House" eps; blue cameo eps
     No frontis or plain frontis
     Poor "war" paper

IV. 1948 - 1954
#1 - #24, including first editions #19 - #24
Regular size with blue weave cover or blue tweed
   cover (begins 1951)
Cameo eps
No frontis or plain frontis
Good paper

1. *Beverly Gray, Freshman*
2. *Beverly Gray, Sophomore*
3. *Beverly Gray, Junior*
4. *Beverly Gray, Senior*
5. *Beverly Gray's Career*
6. *Beverly Gray on a World Cruise*
7. *Beverly Gray in the Orient*
8. *Beverly Gray on a Treasure Hunt* (1938)
9. *Beverly Gray's Return* (1939)
10. *Beverly Gray, Reporter* (1940)
11. *Beverly Gray's Romance* (1941)
12. *Beverly Gray's Quest* (1942)
13. *Beverly Gray's Problem* (1943)
14. *Beverly Gray's Adventure* (1944)
15. *Beverly Gray's Challenge* (1945)
16. *Beverly Gray's Journey* (1946)
17. *Beverly Gray's Assignment* (1947)
18. *Beverly Gray's Mystery* (1948)

19. *Beverly Gray's Vacation* (1949)
20. *Beverly Gray's Fortune* (1950)
21. *Beverly Gray's Secret* (1951)
22. *Beverly Gray's Island Mystery* (1952)
23. *Beverly Gray's Discovery* (1953)
24. *Beverly Gray's Scoop* (1954)

## C. Clover Books
(McLoughlin Bros.)

V. 1955+
#18 - #25, including first edition of #25
Shiny, cellophane-covered picture cover
Rounded or flat spines
Plain eps
Plain frontis
Poor paper

G-18. *Beverly Gray's Mystery*
G-19. *Beverly Gray's Vacation*
G-20. *Beverly Gray's Fortune*
G-21. *Beverly Gray's Secret*
G-22. *Beverly Gray's Island Mystery*
G-23. *Beverly Gray's Discovery*
G-24. *Beverly Gray's Scoop*
G-25. *Beverly Gray's Surprise* (1955)

# 1. Beverly Gray, Freshman

1934. 249 Pages.

Beverly Gray, daughter of legendary alumni Helen Chadwick, arrives at Vernon College to begin her studies. She has a great many adventures during this term: She is lost in a blizzard, held prisoner by a giant insane hermit woman, escapes and falls into a bear pit, and is stalked in the snow by a killer bear. The mystery she solves is the cause of the strange behavior of her roommate, Shirley Parker, who begins to change after Beverly carries her from a burning dormitory building.

The unaccredited paintings used on the first five Beverly Gray dust jackets show scenes that look like they are from a period earlier than the early 1930s of the stories. The first cover shows Beverly wearing formal clothing and high heels while she is carrying Shirley. This is an accurate depiction of college fashions of the time.

| | |
|---|---|
| Format I. | $5.00-$55.00 |
| Format II. | $4.00-$30.00 |
| Format III. | $3.00-$25.00 |
| Format IV. | $3.00-$25.00 |

**1.** (Burt & G&D)

**2.** (Burt & G&D)

**3.** (Burt & G&D)

**4.** (Burt & G&D)

## 2. Beverly Gray, Sophomore

1934. 256 Pages.

Beverly Gray's career is determined in her second year at Vernon. She becomes a reporter for the school newspaper, *The Comet*. She meets airplane pilot and Secret Agent Larry Owens. While looking for news, Beverly uncovers a ring of drug smugglers operating out of a secret room in the mysterious old Horler Mansion.

| | |
|---|---|
| Format I. | $5.00-$55.00 |
| Format II. | $4.00-$30.00 |
| Format III. | $3.00-$25.00 |
| Format IV. | $3.00-$25.00 |

## 3. Beverly Gray, Junior

1934. 254 Pages.

Beverly is kidnapped and held in a gypsy wagon for several weeks until she is finally found and rescued by her friends on page 134. The mystery element of the book is solved and then there are more than 100 pages of various adventures involving dangerous winter sports. Her college friends in the Alpha Delta Sorority become even closer when they elect Beverly president and the summer break begins at Vernon.

| | |
|---|---|
| Format I. | $5.00-$55.00 |
| Format II. | $4.00-$30.00 |
| Format III. | $3.00-$25.00 |
| Format IV. | $3.00-$25.00 |

## 4. Beverly Gray, Senior

1934. 253 Pages.

The Forsythe Film Company comes to Vernon to make a movie about college life. Beverly writes the script and Shirley becomes the star of the movie. Somebody is sabotaging the film and Shirley is kidnapped. Beverly solves these problems and by the end of the book bids "Auld Lang Syne" to Vernon.

| | |
|---|---|
| Format I. | $5.00-$55.00 |
| Format II. | $4.00-$30.00 |
| Format III. | $3.00-$25.00 |
| Format IV. | $3.00-$25.00 |

# 5. Beverly Gray's Career

1935. 254 Pages.

Beverly begins to work in New York as a reporter for the *Herald Tribune* and shares an apartment with Shirley, Lenora and Lois. Beverly solves mysteries connected with the theft of jewels belonging to Omar el-Hamel, who is described as a Hindu.

| | |
|---|---|
| Format I. | $5.00-$55.00 |
| Format II. | $4.00-$30.00 |
| Format III. | $3.00-$25.00 |
| Format IV. | $3.00-$25.00 |

Note: The Format I cloth cover of this book is stamped: "Beverly Gray Career." The A.L. Burt edition is probably the same.

# 6. Beverly Gray at the World's Fair
(A.L. Burt)

1935. 250 Pages.

This one is the "holy grail" of Beverly Gray books. It was printed only by A.L. Burt, as Grosset & Dunlap supposedly thought that the title dated it too much and dropped it when they took over the series from Burt. Page 17 of the following book, *Beverly Gray on a World Cruise*, refers to *Beverly Gray at the World's Fair* and Beverly's adventures in Chicago in all Grosset & Dunlap printings of that book. In *Beverly Gray's Return*, page 143, Connie Elwood reminds her friends of the time they went to the World's Fair in Chicago. When Beverly was at the "Century of Progress Exposition," she was involved with the mystery of a diver who was killed by an air gun, which could also be a reason to drop the title from the juvenile list.

The dust jacket art on the cover of this book also makes *Beverly Gray at the World's Fair* a collectible for those who look for World's Fair memorabilia, as it is a scene from the Chicago Exhibition of 1933 to 1934.

| | |
|---|---|
| Format I. | $75.00+-$200.00+ |

# 7. Beverly Gray on a World Cruise
(A.L. Burt)
# 6. Beverly Gray on a World Cruise
(Grosset & Dunlap)

1936. 247 Pages.

Beverly's wealthy friend, Roger Garrett, takes her, Jim Stanton, Paul Benson, Lenora Whitehill, Shirley Parker and Roger's aunt, Miss Ernwood (as chaperone), on a cruise around the world on his yacht, the *Susabella.* Jim falls overboard, is lost at sea and later ends up in London, where Beverly meets Count Alexis de Franchiny and becomes infatuated with him. Rich Terry Cartwright joins the friends in London and Lois Mason joins them in Paris. Beverly learns that her

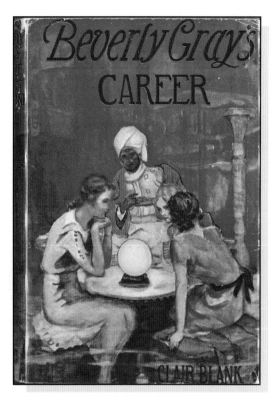

**5.** (Burt & G&D)

**6.** (Burt)

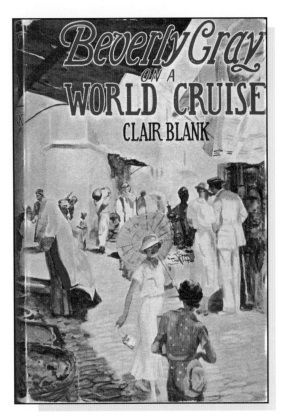

**7.** (Burt) **6.** (G&D)

first book is published, giving her the money to continue the trip. The group acquires half of a treasure map.

The friends were in Paris on Armistice Day, November 11 (1935?). Roger, Beverly, Jim and Shirley rented a plane and flew to Belgium where Roger visited the grave of his brother, George, who was just seventeen years old when he was buried in Flanders Field, having been killed in "the World War." While they were at George's grave, Beverly commented, "And some people want war today. Why?" Jim replied, "As long as there are nations struggling for power and world supremacy there will be war." (Very few young people reading the Beverly Gray series in 1936, when this book was written, would have been concerned with another world war, so it is amazing that Grosset & Dunlap editors left this sequence in the book.)

Much of the plot of this story is continued in the following book, *Beverly Gray in the Orient*, which is continued in the next one, *Beverly Gray on a Treasure Hunt*, which continues in *Beverly Gray's Return*, and that one, in turn, is completed *in Beverly Gray, Reporter*. This crossover of plots took place at the same time the series changed publishers.

| | |
|---|---|
| Format I. | $7.00-$60.00 |
| Format II. | $4.00-$30.00 |
| Format III. | $3.00-$25.00 |
| Format IV. | $3.00-$25.00 |

## 8. Beverly Gray in the Orient (A.L. Burt)
## 7. Beverly Gray in the Orient

(Grosset & Dunlap)

1937. 251 Pages.

The *Susabella* and its passengers continue through the Mediterranean and the Suez Canal to India. Lois is pushed into the sea by an unknown hand and Beverly is pitched into the Ganges when a riverboat sinks. Count Alexis kidnaps Beverly and Jim and they escape, to be plagued with more pursuants in China. Is somebody after that half map from the previous book?

Note: Both *Beverly Gray on a World Cruise* and *Beverly Gray in the Orient* have the same style watercolor art on the dust jacket. Both are busy scenes in pastel colors and are the best art of the series. The artist is not credited, as was the case on the earlier books.

| | |
|---|---|
| Format I. | $7.00-$60.00+ |
| Format II. | $4.00-$30.00 |
| Format III. | $3.00-$25.00 |
| Format IV. | $3.00-$25.00 |

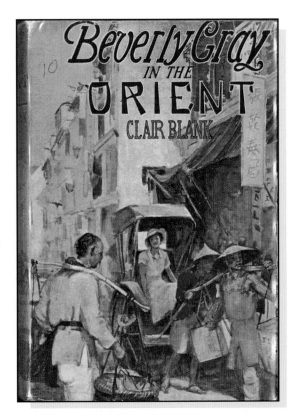

**8.** (Burt) **7.** (G&D)

## 8. Beverly Gray on a Treasure Hunt

1938. 243 Pages.

The *Susabella* sails to a Pacific island where Beverly locates the treasure described on the map mentioned in the two previous books. She is then captured by cannibals, escapes, is caught by Count Alexis, escapes again, and goes back to China where she is assigned by the *Tribune* to report on the Sino-Japanese War. Nikki Abbot, a stranded dancer, joins Beverly and her friends on the *Susabella* and they sail to Hawaii.

| | |
|---|---|
| Format II. | $5.00-$40.00 |
| Format III. | $3.00-$25.00 |
| Format IV. | $3.00-$25.00 |

## 9. Beverly Gray's Return

1939. 251 Pages.

The Beverly Gray who is onboard the *Susabella* is an impostor that Nikki has placed there. Part of her reasoning for this is that she has escaped from the country of Corona, where she is supposed to be queen against her wishes. We are left with a bigger mystery at the end of the book: What is happening with Rosita who is really Rosalie Arnold with amnesia?

| | |
|---|---|
| Format II. | $5.00-$40.00 |
| Format III. | $3.00-$25.00 |
| Format IV. | $3.00-$25.00 |

## 10. Beverly Gray, Reporter

1940. 239 Pages.

Rosalie Arnold's memory returns. Beverly becomes involved with spies who are attempting to steal military plans.

Format II.
$5.00-$40.00
Format III.
$3.00-$25.00
Format IV.
$3.00-$25.00

**8.** (G&D)

**9.** (G&D)

**10.** (G&D)

**11.** (G&D)

**12.** (G&D)

**13.** (G&D)

## 11. Beverly Gray's Romance

1941. 250 Pages.

This book opens with Lenora, Lois, Connie and Kathleen strolling around the "World's Fair Grounds." No explanation is given, but this must be the New York World's Fair of 1939 to 1940. Shortly after this, Beverly and her friends go to Rest Haven on the coast of Maine for vacation. In Maine, they solve mysteries connected with a cave stockpiled with weapons, spies and government agents. At the end of the book, Larry presents Beverly with a diamond engagement ring.

| | |
|---|---|
| Format II. | $5.00-$45.00 |
| Format III. | $3.00-$25.00 |
| Format IV. | $3.00-$25.00 |

## 12. Beverly Gray's Quest

1942. 220 Pages.

Beverly learns that her book is going to be made into a movie and that she will make a lot of money from it. Larry turns up missing in South America and the friends travel there on the *Susabella* to find him. The emerald shown in the picture on the dust jacket is part of this mystery.

| | |
|---|---|
| Format II. | $5.00-$45.00 |
| Format III. | $3.00-$25.00 |
| Format IV. | $3.00-$25.00 |

Note: *Beverly Gray's Romance* and *Beverly Gray's Quest* had dust jacket designs that were similar.

## 13. Beverly Gray's Problem

1943. 214 Pages.

It appears that True Torston stole a Buddha figure from Beatrice Colfax's mansion. Unpleasant Kay Merrill, a reporter on the *Sun,* causes problems for Beverly. Shirley (as Dale Arden) stars in Beverly's play, *Angels Arise,* on Broadway.

Note: *Beverly Gray's Problem* is the shortest book yet of the series. It only has 214 pages and twenty-three lines of type per page. (*Beverly Gray, Freshman* had 249 pages and twenty-eight lines of type.) There are only fifteen chapters in it. The early ones had around twenty-five. This mystery and the next two, *Beverly Gray's Adventure* and *Beverly Gray's Challenge,* have a uniform style of dust jacket.

| | |
|---|---|
| Format III. | $3.00-$25.00 |
| Format IV. | $3.00-$25.00 |

# 14. Beverly Gray's Adventure

1944. 213 Pages.

Beverly is working as a government agent and, as such, becomes a guest in the home of Kurt Kresloff, a suspected enemy agent. The Alpha Delta girls meet Harriet who pretends to know Beverly in order to get a part in her play, *Angels Arise,* in which Shirley is appearing on Broadway.

Note: This mystery and the next one, *Beverly Gray's Challenge*, have dust jackets and frontispieces by Russell H. Tandy, the artist who did the first twenty-six Nancy Drew books, except for one cover (*The Clue of the Broken Locket*). This makes it appear as if Grosset & Dunlap was attempting to make the Beverly Gray Series more successful.

| | |
|---|---|
| Format III. | $3.00-$25.00 |
| Format IV. | $3.00-$25.00 |

# 15. Beverly Gray's Challenge

1945. 207 Pages.

Beverly, Shirley, Lenora and Lois set off in Beverly's car from New York to Montana, where Shirley inherited the Lazy Y Ranch. In the West, the girls encounter many problems from someone who is probably after the ranch himself.

| | |
|---|---|
| Format III. | $3.00-$25.00 |
| Format IV. | $3.00-$25.00 |

# 16. Beverly Gray's Journey

1946. 209 Pages.

Beverly Gray's journey is to England to search for Larry Owens, from whom she has not heard in more than a month. Beverly discovers that Larry is with yet another Beverly Gray impostor.

| | |
|---|---|
| Format III. | $3.00-$25.00 |
| Format IV. | $3.00-$25.00 |

Note: The books in the Beverly Gray Series from Volume 16 through 25 have a common printing style for the title and author's name on the cover; however the cover artwork is still many unique styles of illustration and Beverly looks like a different person on each one.

**14.** (G&D)

**15.** (G&D)

**16.** (G&D)

**17.** (G&D)          **18.** (G&D & Clover)

## 17. Beverly Gray's Assignment

1947. 212 Pages.

Beverly's colleague, reporter Kay Merrill, disappears and Beverly and Lenora search for her in New Orleans. Kay is restored to her friends and they also secure a lost fortune for new friend Doreen Hampton.

|  |  |
|---|---|
| Format III. | $3.00-$25.00 |
| Format IV. | $3.00-$25.00 |

## 18. Beverly Gray's Mystery

1948. 207 Pages.

Indian Prince Houssain's "precious Star of the East" is stolen. An evil Hindu, Ram, is involved in this problem. Beverly solves this mystery and also the mystery of what the "Star of the East" actually is.

|  |  |
|---|---|
| Format III. | $3.00-$25.00 |
| Format IV. | $3.00-$30.00 |
| Format V. | $2.50-$15.00 |

## 19. Beverly Gray's Vacation

**19.** (G&D & Clover)

1949. 212 Pages.

Beverly and her friends set off on another "gay cruise" on the *Susabella*. Beverly finds the solution to her new friend Phyllis Tanner's problems in the freezing wilds of Canada.

|  |  |
|---|---|
| Format IV. | $4.00-$30.00 |
| Format V. | $2.50-$15.00 |

Note: Although this volume in the series has 212 pages, it has only fifteen chapters.

# 20. Beverly Gray's Fortune

1950. 207 Pages.

The *Susabella* sails to Hawaii with Beverly, Lois, Lenora, Shirley, Roger Garrett, Larry Owens, Jim Stanton, Terry Cartwright, the Chinese cook Woo Fang and the chaperone of the group, Roger's aunt, Miss Ernwood. This is the same group who sailed on the *Susabella* in the volumes from *Beverly Gray on a World Cruise* to *Beverly Gray's Return* (Grosset & Dunlap Volumes 6 through 9). In Hawaii, Beverly solves a mystery that had baffled the people of Hawaii for more than a year and changes the ill luck attached to the fortune she received there.

Note: This is the first volume in the series to carry the spine symbol picture of Beverly, which was continued through the remainder of the set.

|  |  |
|---|---|
| Format IV. | $4.00-$30.00 |
| Format V. | $2.50-$15.00 |

# 21. Beverly Gray's Secret

1951. 212 Pages.

Beverly learned by cablegram while she was on the *Susabella* in Hawaii that Mr. Blaine had fired her from her position on the *Tribune*. She flew back to New York to solve this riddle and then flew to Miami for more investigations.

|  |  |
|---|---|
| Format IV. | $4.00-$30.00 |
| Format V. | $2.50-$15.00 |

# 22. Beverly Gray's Island Mystery

1952. 179 Pages.

A month after leaving their friends on the *Susabella*, Beverly and Larry Owens are still in Miami after solving the previous mystery. Beverly receives a letter from Lenora telling her that a Professor Green from Vernon College, the girls' Alma Mater, has joined the group aboard ship. Then the *Susabella* and all aboard disappear at sea. Beverly flies to an island in the South Pacific to solve this dilemma.

Note how few pages are now in the Beverly Gray Series. The dust jacket for this book depicts the most attractive representation of Beverly of the entire series.

|  |  |
|---|---|
| Format IV. | $4.00-$35.00 |
| Format V. | $2.50-$15.00 |

**20.** (G&D & Clover)

**21.** (G&D & Clover)

**22.** (G&D & Clover)

**23.** (G&D & Clover)

**24.** (G&D & Clover)

**25.** (Clover)

## 23. Beverly Gray's Discovery

1953. 183 Pages.

Shirley Parker shows Beverly a "genuine Dumier" painting that she bought for the house she and Roger will share when they are married. This leads to the study and exposure of fake art masterpieces.

| | |
|---|---|
| Format IV. | $4.00-$40.00 |
| Format V. | $2.50-$15.00 |

## 24. Beverly Gray's Scoop

1954. 184 Pages.

When Frank Stanton dies it appears that Beverly's friend, Jim Stanton, will inherit Frank's fortune, but all sorts of "heirs" come forward, including another Jim Stanton. Who will get the "scoop" on this story, Beverly or Kay Merrill?

| | |
|---|---|
| Format IV. | $4.00-$45.00 |
| Format V. | $2.50-$15.00 |

## 25. Beverly Gray's Surprise

1955. 182 Pages.

This mystery opens at the wedding of Lois Mason and Jim Stanton. Another friend, Mike McKay, comes to the wedding but hides outside until Beverly spots him and learns why he does not want to be seen. She, Lenora and Larry travel to Montana to clear Mike of suspicion in a robbery. The last paragraph in the book is:

"So it was on a happy note the next morning that the four long-time friends and Mr. Brewster began their cross-country journey back to New York, where still more excitement and adventures awaited them."

But this was the last book in the series. Grosset & Dunlap copyrighted this book and must have intended to publish it, as it is listed on the back flap of the Judy Bolton book *The Clue of the Ruined Castle*, also published in 1955, but the book is only available in the Clover picture cover edition.

| | |
|---|---|
| Format V. | $3.00-$20.00 |

# CHAPTER 6

# Kay Tracey Mystery Stories

The Kay Tracey series of mystery stories was the Stratemeyer Syndicate's girl detective books for the Cupples & Leon Company from 1934 to 1942. The eighteen-volume series has many similarities to the Nancy Drew books from Grosset & Dunlap. At the time, each series had twenty-five chapters and a little more than 200 pages. Like Nancy Drew, Kay is also a sixteen-year-old with only one parent and her two best friends help her with mystery solving. Most of the Kay Tracey books were written by Mildred A. Wirt from Stratemeyer outlines at the same time she was doing the Nancy Drew books, although it seems as if there is more Wirt in the Kay Tracey series than in the Nancy Drew one. Wirt is credited with Volumes 3 to 14 of the Kay Tracey books, using the Cupples & Leon numbering of the set.

The Kay Tracey mystery plots are sometimes unbelievable and too frequently deal with characters, especially villains, who are rather broad in interpretation, like many found in the Penny Parker series by Mildred A. Wirt. Too many of Kay's experiences involve spooky mansions (a staple of girl detectives' problems) and persons who are attempting to unjustly claim an inheritance or fortune belonging to a more worthy individual, which a great many Nancy Drew plots also entail. Many of the Kay Tracey books could have been Nancy Drew mysteries with name changes and minor adjustments, as the basic premises are so similar. One wonders if Mrs. Wirt or the Stratemeyer Syndicate saved the better plot situations for Nancy Drew and used the second-rate ones for Kay Tracey.

Dark-haired, brown-eyed Kay lives with her widowed mother and Cousin Bill, a thirty-year-old lawyer. Her best friends are the Worth twins, one blonde and one brunette. Kay has a steady boyfriend. With minor changes, all this could be about Nancy Drew. One major difference is that Kay has an enemy, troublemaker Ethel Eaton (called Chris Eaton in revised editions).

The first Kay Tracey series was probably canceled because of World War II and the paper shortage problem and the fact that Cupples & Leon books could not compete with the more dominant Grosset & Dunlap in the juvenile market; however, no series of juvenile mysteries has had as many resurrections

as the Kay Tracey Mystery Stories. In 1951, they were released as a fifteen-volume set by Doubleday & Company's Garden City Books. In the late 1950s, Books, Inc., published this same set of fifteen books, in a different order, followed with the same books as a paperback edition and later a picture cover set. In 1960, the Kay Tracey Mysteries became the first major paperback girls' series with eight volumes from Berkley Publishing. In 1978, Lamplight Publishing, Inc., did a six-volume set in the picture cover format (more about that later) and, beginning in 1980, the same six books were a Bantam series in two different formats. The latest version is the British paperback set of 1984 from William Collins & Co. that is again the same six volumes. The end result is that there are more distinct American publishers of the Stratemeyer Syndicate's Kay Tracey books than any other juvenile series of modern times.

In 1951, and again in 1980, the Kay Tracey Mysteries were updated with minor changes. The different companies that published Kay Tracey books placed them in a different sequence. This does not matter, as no book furthers the lives of the characters in chronological order, nor is any book a sequel of the previous volume, unlike the continuity and time progression found in the Judy Bolton books. The Kay Tracey mysteries could be placed in just about any order, as the Nancy Drew books were when published in England. The only book that was substantially revised and changed is the first Cupples & Leon book of 1934, *The Secret of the Red Scarf*, when it was published by Garden City in 1952.

## The Kay Tracey Books

The Kay Tracey books have interesting and unusual formats.

The Cupples & Leon set, in four different formats, began as "thick" books with the heavy paper that was a standard in the juvenile market at the time and they cost 50 cents, as did Grosset & Dunlap books. The early ones had good cloth covers with a

glossy picture inside. The dust jacket picture is unique in that it looks like an open book with a scene from the story and a sample page opposite.

Even though Kay is described in the books as dark-haired she is shown on most of the book dust jacket pictures and picture covers as a blonde or redhead. The Cupples & Leon books usually showed her with blonde hair. Betty and Wilma, Kay's best friends, have many different shades of hair on the cover pictures of books from various publishers.

The cover pictures I like best are the ones on the Garden City books from the 1950s. This set was designed like the Grosset & Dunlap books in that the dust jackets were colorful and showed an exciting scene from the mystery. The books were not for sale in places that carried Grosset & Dunlap books. I bought mine in a cigar/stationary store that carried some adult books.

The cover designs from the Garden City books were also used for the three different sets by Books, Inc. These cover pictures had the volume number and the wording "Garden City" crudely scribbled over on the spines of the dust jackets; otherwise the cover was identical.

The Berkley paperback books of the 1960s have new cover art. This set has two different cover designs, mainly affecting the banner at the top, to designate that the books are either "Berkley Highland Books" or "Berkley Medallion Books."

To me the most interesting set of all is the Lamplight Publishing set. The six picture cover books in this set appear to have the same cover art as the Garden City/Books, Inc., ones, but they don't.

The Lamplight books have a richer and lighter color tone than the earlier books and include a bit more picture. Look closely. They are not the same art. They are very good copies of the earlier books. The differences can be seen most clearly in minute details, such as the lantern to the left and the blossoms in the plant on the table of *The Green Cameo Mystery*, as one example. Even the printing of the titles on the covers seems identical, but it is not that much alike upon closer inspection. This can be seen clearly if the two different spines are compared side-by-side and by noting that the title lettering on the front of the book is actually slightly different fonts. This has to be one of the more interesting phenomenons of juvenile literature cover design. The back of these picture cover books mentions that this is "the first six novels in a series…," but there were never more. Also noteworthy about Lamplight books is how easily the hinges become separated from the interior of these books.

The Bantam and Armada paperback books each have new and distinctive cover art. Both are very good, although the Armada paperbacks are the only ones that show Kay as a brunette, which she was always supposed to be.

# Kay Tracey Book Formats

## Cupples & Leon Co.

I. 1934 - 1942
#1 - #18, including first editions #1 - #18
Thick yellow cloth cover with red lettering
Page tops w/red tinting have whiter paper (earlier ?)
Cameo designs on eps
Glossy frontis
Good paper
Black bars in dust jacket design
Question mark symbol on dj spine

II. 1943(?)
#1 - #18
Thin tan cover with red lettering
Cameo design eps
Glossy frontis
Good paper
Volume number added to dj spine

III. Mid 1940s
#1 - #18 (?)
Thin mustard yellow with rough finish
Book is shorter
Red cover lettering
Plain weave design eps
Glossy or plain frontis
Poor paper
Each volume has different dj spine symbol
Black bars removed from djs
Volume number on dj spine

IV. Late 1940s
#1 - #18
Thin mustard yellow with smooth finish
Short book
Red cover lettering
Weave design eps
Plain, modernized frontis
Poor paper
Dj spines in various colors
No black bars
Volume number on spine of dj

1. *The Secret of the Red Scarf* (1934)
2. *The Strange Echo* (1934)
3. *The Mystery of the Swaying Curtains* (1935)
4. *The Shadow on the Door* (1935)
5. *The Six Fingered Glove Mystery* (1936)
6. *The Green Cameo Mystery* (1936)
7. *The Secret at the Windmill* (1937)
8. *Beneath the Crimson Brier Bush* (1937)
9. *The Message in the Sand Dunes* (1938)
10. *The Murmuring Portrait* (1938)
11. *When the Key Turned* (1939)
12. *In the Sunken Garden* (1939)
13. *The Forbidden Tower* (1940)
14. *The Sacred Feather* (1940)
15. *The Lone Footprint* (1941)
16. *The Double Disguise* (1941)
17. *The Mansion of Secrets* (1942)
18. *The Mysterious Neighbors* (1942)

**1.**

**2.**

**3.**

**4.** *Kenneth Hopping Collection.*

**5.**

**6.** *Kenneth Hopping Collection.*

**7.** *Kenneth Hopping Collection.*

**8.** *Kenneth Hopping Collection.*

**9.** *Kenneth Hopping Collection.*

**10.** *Kenneth Hopping Collection.*

**11.** *Kenneth Hopping Collection.*

**12.**

**13.** *Kenneth Hopping Collection.*

**14.**

**15.**

**16.** *Kenneth Hopping Collection.*

**17.** *Lorraine Rogers Collection.*

**18.** *Kenneth Hopping Collection.*

## B. Garden City Books
### (Doubleday & Company, Inc.)

V.  1951 to 1952
#1 - #15 (Different than Cupples & Leon)
Updated editions of originals
Red cloth-like cover
Three girls w/collie eps
Plain frontis
Good paper
New art on wrap dj
Cameo logo on dj spine
Number (Kl, and so on) on spine

K1.  *The Mansion of Secrets* (1951)
K2.  *The Sacred Feather* (1951)
K3.  *The Six Fingered Glove Mystery* (1951)
K4.  *In the Sunken Garden* (1951)
K5.  *The Mysterious Neighbors* (1951)
K6.  *When the Key Turned* (1951)
K7.  *The Double Disguise* (1952)
K8.  *The Secret at the Windmill* (1952)
K9.  *The Murmuring Portrait* (1952)
K10.  *The Lone Footprint* (1952)
K11.  *The Message in the Sand Dunes* (1952)
K12.  *The Crimson Brier Bush* (1952)
K13.  *The Green Cameo Mystery* (1952)
K14.  *The Strange Echo* (1952)
K15.  *The Secret of the Red Scarf* (1952)

Garden City **K1.**  Books, Inc. **3.**

Garden City **K3.**  Books, Inc. **4.**

Garden City **K2.**  Books, Inc. **1.**

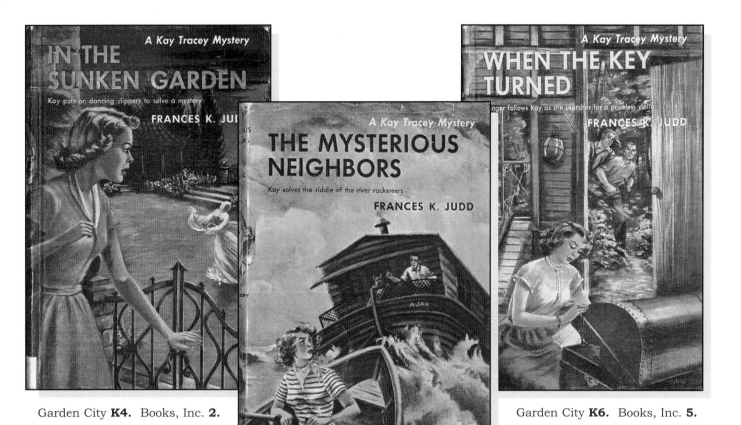

Garden City **K4.**  Books, Inc. **2.**

Garden City **K6.**  Books, Inc. **5.**

Garden City  **K5.**
Books, Inc. **6.**

Garden City **K7.**  Books, Inc. **10.**

Garden City **K9.**  Books, Inc. **9.**

Garden City **K8.**  Books, Inc. **8.**

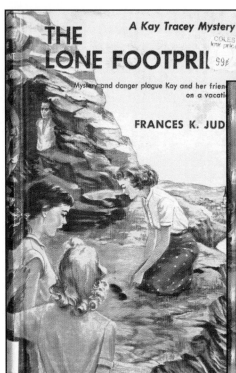

Garden City **K10.** Books, Inc. **7.**

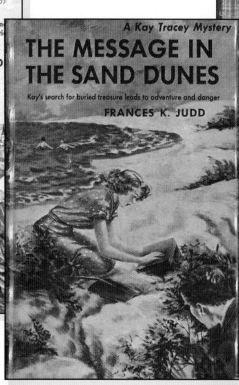

Garden City **K11.**
Books, Inc. **11.**

Garden City **K12.** Books, Inc. **12.**

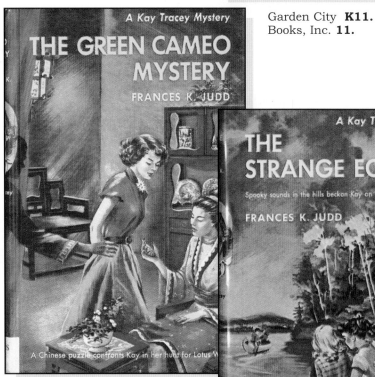

Garden City **K13.** Books, Inc. **13.**

Garden City **K14.** Books, Inc. **14.**

Garden City **K15.** Books, Inc. **15.**

# C. Books, Inc.

VI. Late 1950s
#1 - #15 (Different than Garden City) but same printing
  plates used
Red, green, aqua, blue covers
Slightly taller than Garden City
Blank eps
Plain frontis
Poor paper
Same djs as Garden City
Number and "Garden City" blocked out on spine

VII. Circa 1960
#1 - #15 (Books, Inc., numbers)
Paperback edition of the above
Same covers, printing plates as Garden City & Books,
  Inc., hardbacks
Spine same as dj versions
Plain frontis
Very poor paper

VIII. Circa 1974
#1 - #15 (Books, Inc., numbers)
Picture cover edition of the above
Same covers, printing plates as the above
Same size as Garden City editions
"Books, Inc." at spine bottom
Blank eps
Plain frontis
Good paper

1. *The Sacred Feather*
2. *In the Sunken Garden*
3. *The Mansion of Secrets*
4. *The Six Fingered Glove Mystery*
5. *When the Key Turned*
6. *The Mysterious Neighbors*
7. *The Lone Footprint*
8. *The Secret of the Windmill*
9. *The Murmuring Portrait*
10. *The Double Disguise*
11. *The Message in the Sand Dunes*
12. *The Crimson Brier Bush*
13. *The Green Cameo Mystery*
14. *The Strange Echo*
15. *The Secret of the Red Scarf*

## D. Berkley Publishing Corporation
(Berkley Medalion and
Berkley Highland Books)

IX. 1960 - 1968
#1 - #8 (Berkley numbers)
(Same text as above, but reset for smaller
size book)
Mass-market paperback books
New cover art

1. *The Sacred Feather* (1960)
2. *The Mansion of Secrets* (1960)
3. *The Six Fingered Glove Mystery* (1960)
4. *The Mysterious Neighbors* (1960)
5. *The Green Cameo Mystery* (1961)
6. *The Double Disguise* (1961)
7. *The Strange Echo* (1964)
8. *The Message in the Sand Dunes* (1964)

Berkley Publishing
Corporation **1.**

Berkley Publishing Corporation **2.**

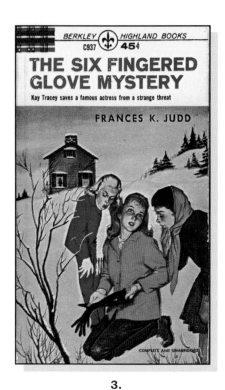

3.

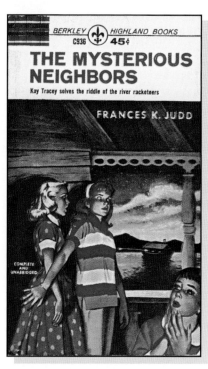

4.

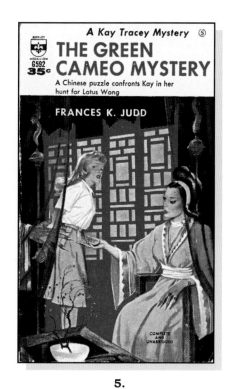

5.

6.

7.

8.

## E. Lamplight Publishing Inc.

X.  1978
   #1 - #6 (Lamplight set)
   Picture covers
   Square spine
   Cover is new copy of Garden City
      and Books, Inc., covers
   Same text and frontis as Garden
      City and Books, Inc.
   Kay w/curtain eps
   Good paper

1. *The Mansion of Secrets*
2. *The Six Fingered Glove Mystery*
3. *The Double Disguise*
4. *In the Sunken Garden*
5. *The Green Cameo Mystery*
6. *The Message in the Sand Dunes*

1.

2.

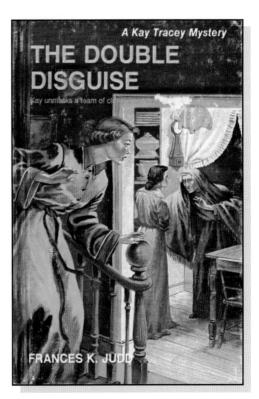

3.

4.

5.

6.

## F. Bantam Skylark Books

XII.   1980
     #1 - #6 (Bantam numbers)
     Large size paperbacks
     Text is revised and modernized
     Same plain frontis as Garden City editions
     New cover art

1. *The Double Disguise*
2. *In the Sunken Garden*
3. *The Six Fingered Glove Mystery*
4. *The Mansion of Secrets*
5. *The Green Cameo Mystery*
6. *The Message in the Sand Dunes*

## G. Bantam Special Book Club Edition

XII.   1981
     #1 - #6 (same as above)
     Mass-market paperback
     All is the same as above, except for size

1. *The Double Disguise*
2. *In the Sunken Garden*
3. *The Six Fingered Glove Mystery*
4. *The Mansion of Secrets*
5. *The Green Cameo Mystery*
6. *The Message in the Sand Dunes*

1.

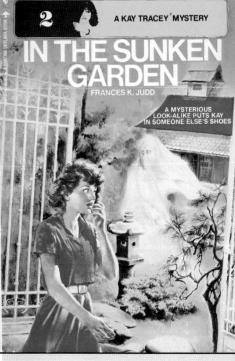

2.

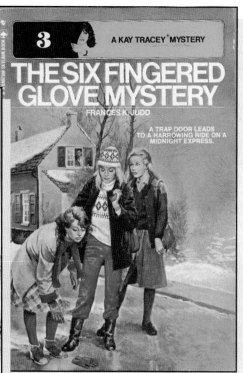

3.

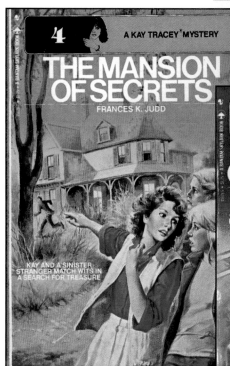

4.

5.

6.

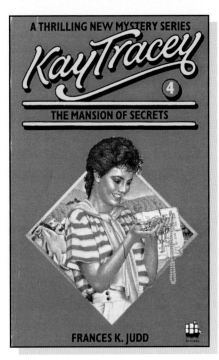

**4.**

**H. Armada (William Collins & Co., Ltd.)**

XIII. 1984
   #1 - #6 (same list as above)
   Mass-market paperback
   Text is same as above but Anglicized w/minor
      changes
   Different pagination
   No frontis
   New cover art

1. *The Double Disguise*
2. *In the Sunken Garden*
3. *The Six Fingered Glove Mystery*
4. *The Mansion of Secrets*
5. *The Green Cameo Mystery*
6. *The Message in the Sand Dunes*

# Kay Tracey Book Values

The values for the Kay Tracey books pretty much fall into the Format in which they are available. They are given below, and the brief synopsis of each book lists in which formats they are available.

| | | |
|---|---|---|
| Format I. | Cupples & Leon | $4.00-$35.00 |
| | Volumes 15 - 18 | $5.00-$50.00+ |
| Format II. | " | $4.00-$30.00 |
| Format III. | " | $3.00-$25.00 |
| Format IV. | " | $3.00-$20.00 |
| Format V. | Garden City | $2.00-$30.00 |
| Format VI. | Books, Inc.  (Dust Jacket) | $2.00-$20.00 |
| Format VII. | "  (Paperback) | $3.00-$8.00 |
| Format VIII. | "  (Picture Cover) | $4.00-$25.00 |
| Format IX. | Berkley | $3.00-$10.00 |
| Format X. | Lamplight | $4.00-$25.00 |
| Format XI. | Bantam Skylark | $3.00-$8.00 |
| Format XII. | Bantam Book Club | $3.00-$8.00 |
| Format XIII. | Armada | $3.00-$10.00 |

# Kay Tracey Books, Volumes 1 to 18

## 1. The Secret of the Red Scarf

1934 Edition. 206 Pages.

Kay searches for Helene Ludlow who, as Barbara Brown, ran away from home to become a stage actress.

Formats I, II, III, IV.

1952 Edition. 192 Pages.

The plot has many changes from the original edition. Now the boy who is searching for his sister has amnesia and the sister, Helene Caldwell, looks like Kay.

Formats V, VI, VII, VIII.

## 2. The Strange Echo

1934 Edition. 206 Pages.

Kay helps a "foreign woman" and searches for pages stolen from a rare book.

Formats I, II, III, IV.

1952 Edition. 192 Pages.

A revised and updated version of the 1934 original.

Formats V, VI, VII, VIII.
Format IX has 160 pages.

## 3. The Mystery of the Swaying Curtains

1935 Edition. 208 Pages.

Kay helps Sissy gain a lost fortune and catches a thief. She also finds the missing Mrs. Barling who found a new husband. (The climbing on roofs and trees sequences are similar to those in the Judy Bolton book *The Clue of the Broken Wing* in 1958.)

Formats I, II, III, IV.

## 4. The Shadow on the Door

1935 Edition. 204 Pages.

Kay searches for an illegal alien, a robber and a con artist.

Formats I, II, III, IV.

## 5. The Six Fingered Glove Mystery

1936 Edition. 203 Pages.

A glove with six fingers is the clue to the kidnapping of actress Beatrice Ball.

Formats I, II, III, IV.

1951 Updated edition. 203 Pages.

Formats V, VI, VII, VIII, X.

Note: The Books, Inc. books have the plain frontispiece from Cupples & Leon as well as the updated one from Garden City Books.

Format IX has 174 pages.

1980 Updated edition. 166 Pages.

Formats XI, XII.
Format XIII.

## 6. The Green Cameo Mystery

1936 Edition. 211 Pages.

Cara Noma, a medium, is frightening Mrs. Wong at the laundry with the green cameo curse.

Formats I, II, III, IV.

1951 Updated edition. 188 Pages.

Formats V, VI, VII, VIII, X.
Format IX has 142 pages.

1980 Updated edition. 165 Pages.

Formats XI, XII.
Format XIII.

## 7. The Secret at the Windmill

1937 Edition. 203 Pages.

Kay aids Juliana Van Camp whose guardian is cheating her.

Formats I, II, III, IV.

1952 Updated edition. 203 Pages.

Formats V, VI, VII, VIII.

## 8. Beneath the Crimson Brier Bush

1937 Edition. 206 Pages.

Kay finds a baby under a bush while visiting with Aunt Jessie. Although Jessie has mental problems, she insists on keeping the baby and raising it her way. Kay searches for the baby's father.

Formats I, II, III, IV.

1952 Updated edition. **The Crimson Brier Bush**. 206 Pages.

Formats V, VI, VII, VIII.

## 9. The Message in the Sand Dunes

1938 Edition. 204 Pages.

Kay comes to the aid of two elderly spinsters when lightening strikes their home and sets it on fire. Henrietta Crowley insists that she will rescue a heavy cabinet and refuses help with it. Kay finds a manuscript and brings a fortune to the Crowley sisters.

Formats I, II, III, IV.

1952 Updated edition. 204 Pages.

Formats V, VI, VII, VIII, X.
Format IX has 158 pages.

1980 Updated edition. 164 Pages.
Formats XI, XII.
Format XIII.

## 10. The Murmuring Portrait

1938 Edition. 204 Pages.

A passing tramp tosses snakes into the food at Kay's picnic. Kay investigates the reason for this strange behavior and learns that he is the heir to a fortune.

Formats I, II, III, IV.

1952 Updated edition. 204 Pages.

Formats V, VI, VII, VIII.

## 11. When the Key Turned

1939 Edition. 204 Pages.

Kay is locked in a trunk and is threatened with a bear in a case involving a stolen violin.

Formats I, II, III, IV.

1951 Updated edition. 204 Pages.

Formats V, VI, VII, VIII.

## 12. In the Sunken Garden

1939 Edition. 210 Pages.

Kay is mistaken for a missing girl. She searches for her double who is being held against her will at a dancing school.

Formats I, II, III, IV.

1951 Updated edition. 210 Pages.

Formats V, VI, VII, VIII, X.

1980 Updated edition. 166 Pages.

Formats XI, XII.
Format XIII.

## 13. The Forbidden Tower

1940 Edition. 212 Pages.

Kay comes in conflict with her enemy, Ethel Eaton, while on vacation in Florida, where she investigates a strange tower.

Formats I, II, III, IV.

## 14. The Sacred Feather

1940 Edition. 211 Pages.

A tramp, Abou Menzel, comes to the Tracey's back door begging for food. Kay ultimately helps him gain employment in the new Egyptian room of the Brantwood library. In the meantime, she discovers the origin of many arson fires.

Formats I, II, III, IV.

1951 Updated edition. 211 Pages.

Formats V, VI, VII, VIII.
Format IX has 174 pages.

## 15. The Lone Footprint

1941 Edition. 209 Pages.

Kay and her friends, twins Betty and Wilma, go to Owl's Hole to solve the cause of the thwarting of a housing development. Kay also brings a one-legged crook to justice.

Formats I, II, III, IV.

1952 Updated edition. 209 Pages.

Formats V, VI, VII, VIII.

## 16. The Double Disguise

1941 Edition. 212 Pages.

Kay investigates an old house to see if a witch lives there. She also brings thieves of a valuable chemical to justice.

Formats I, II, III, IV.

1952 Updated edition. 212 Pages.

Formats V, VI, VII, VIII, X.
Format IX has 141 pages.

1980 Updated edition. 150 Pages.

Formats XI, XII, XIII.

## 17. The Mansion of Secrets

1942 Edition. 208 Pages.

Kay searches the old Greeley mansion for hidden treasure and matches wits with a sinister stranger.

Formats I, II, III, IV.

1951 Updated edition. 208 Pages.

Formats V, VI, VII, VIII, X.
Format IX has 158 pages.

1980 Updated edition. 165 Pages.

Formats XI, XIII.
Format XIII.

## 18. The Mysterious Neighbors

1942 Edition. 209 Pages.

While on vacation Kay and her friends investigate *The Witch,* a haunted houseboat belonging to Mrs. Chauncey Ball, Cousin Bill's friend.

Formats I, II, III, IV.

1951 Updated edition. 209 Pages.

Formats V, VI, VII, VIII.
Format IX has 157 pages.

# CHAPTER 7

# Penny Parker Mystery Stories

Mildred A. Wirt began the Penny Parker series when the Kay Tracey mysteries that she was doing for the Stratemeyer Syndicate came to an end. At this time she was still working on Nancy Drew books from Harriet Adams outlines. This was during the late 1930s and into the World War II years.

The Penny Parker books have more overt references to the times and more personal opinions from the author than almost any other girls' series books ever did. The Nancy Drew books had almost no reference to the war years. Penny Parker was involved with "sabotage" and "the enemy" on several occasions.

It is not known how much control Mrs. Wirt had over the plots of the Penny Parker books from Cupples & Leon. It is known that she did not have plot control over the Nancy Drew books. Since the two series are so different in tone and style it could be presumed that the Penny Parker stories were much more the creation of Mrs. Wirt than the Nancy Drew books ever were.

On the surface there are many similarities between Penny Parker and Nancy Drew, as there are between Kay Tracey and Nancy Drew. Penny has blue eyes and blonde hair; she is sixteen years old; she lives with a widowed father somewhere in the Midwest; they have a motherly housekeeper; and Penny has her own cars to get around in. Penny is more ambitious than Nancy, as she aspires to be a newspaper reporter (like Beverly Gray) and she solves many of the mysteries so that she can provide copy to her paper, the *Riverview Star*. Penny seems like a nice girl and an honest girl, but it is apparent that she needs money more than many other girl sleuths do.

One huge problem with the Penny Parker series is that they have far more characters (especially criminals) who are ethnic stereotypes and who are described with terrible adjectives and there are many more undereducated rural types who are unknowingly comical than there are in any other girls' series books. All this makes Penny (and Wirt) seem rather prejudiced and intolerant. Much of this could be explained by the emergency situations of the times—World War II—and attitudes towards the "enemy," but other series books in that period avoided these pitfalls. Even in that era it was not considered good taste to call a Chinese person a "Chink" (*The Vanishing Houseboat*) and juvenile literature seldom referred to an older woman as "Old Lady Lear" (*Hoofbeats on the Turnpike*) when this was not the name she was known by.

The Penny Parker Books are eagerly collected today, especially because they are the work of Mildred A. Wirt, and are more valuable as collectors' items than other series books that are better mysteries. Penny Parker books are interesting in that they are a comment on the World War II years in the United States. The plots and stories of the Penny Parker series do not hold up well though. They are unrealistic and often unbelievable. The books are consistent in quality, in which they are not totally lacking, and in entertainment value, as they are the work of a single author, but it is doubtful that they were widely successful and well distributed in their time.

# The Penny Parker Books

Cupples & Leon's Penny Parker books have a style similar to the Kay Tracey books from the same company at the same time, and the opposite series was advertised on the back of the other set of books. The earlier, thick Penny Parkers have a better hard cover and better paper than the later ones in the set. The only complete set of all seventeen books in the same format is the thinner ones with poorer paper inside. These were printed in the mid to late 1940s.

The dust jackets on the Cupples & Leon books are of inferior quality. There is a poor illustration in a palate-shaped format with a plain background color that is a scene from the book. The drawing is rather like a cartoon and is the work of an amateur, although some are credited to a K.S. Woerner. These pictures are mostly black and white with the addition of one other solid color, such as red here and there in the picture. The background color is also the color on the spines of the dust jackets. They are red, green and blue with one purple cover (*Hoofbeats on the Turnpike*) and do not fall in a consistent pattern. Most of the dust jackets I have seen are not varnished, which would have protected the paper and the picture on it. The hard covers are either red or blue and were not produced sequentially in a pattern either.

These rather plain and unattractive covers on the Penny Parker books must have hurt their sales potential. I got my set in a G.C. Murphy "5 and 10 Cent Store" in December 1952 and January 1953 as remaindered items at three for $1.00. Some of the dust jackets had tears on them when they were purchased new from huge piles at the front of the store.

I have never seen copies of the first few Penny Parker books that were reprinted in the late 1950s in a more attractive updated version, nor did I ever see any Cupples & Leon books in any store that sold juvenile books during the time I was young. I have heard that they were more available in larger cities.

Penny Parker books are rather difficult to locate today with dust jackets, or even without dust jackets for that matter, and they sell for higher prices than other sets of girls' series books because of this.

## Penny Parker Book Formats

### Cupples & Leon Co.

I. 1939 - early 1940s
(Early volumes of series)
Thick red or blue cover
Glossy frontis
Good paper
Cartoon-like djs

II. Mid to late 1940s
#1 - #17
Thin red or blue cover
Plain line-drawn frontis
Weave design eps
Poor paper
Unvarnished djs[1] have a different spine symbol for each mystery

III. 1950s (?)
#1 - #4
Thin blue hard backs
New plain frontis
New full-color djs[2]

[1]Grosset & Dunlap book dust jackets had protective varnish over the front picture and spine. This is evidenced by the fact that they are "shiny." Many Cupples & Leon books did not, another reason why their books seem to have less quality than those from Grosset & Dunlap.

[2]See *The Girls' Series Companion*, 1997 Edition, Page P-435.

## Penny Parker Book Values

Values for Penny Parker books are basically within their Format categories. The Formats and Values are given below. Note that Format I is believed to belong to early printings of the books; Format II is from the mid to late 1940s and all Penny Parker books are found in it; no values are given for Format III.

Format I   $5.00-100.00+
Format II   $3.00-75.00+

## 1. Tale of the Witch Doll

1939 Edition. 210 Pages.

Penny helps the actress Helene Harmon who is plagued with the gift of a doll dressed as a witch.

## 2. The Vanishing Houseboat

1939 Edition. 204 Pages.

Penny solves two mysteries: People disappear from "Old Mansion," a boarding house and a poor family has its houseboat stolen. One has to read page 200 to believe what Mud-Cat Joe said when he recovered his boat. He declared, "Them no 'count Chinks sure banged up the River Queen a-plenty."

**1.** *D.J. Layhe Collection.*

**2.**

## 3. Danger at the Drawbridge

1940 Edition. 211 Pages.

Penny is slated to report on a society wedding by the *Star* so that she can gain access to an old castle surrounded by a moat where a possible income tax evader disappeared years earlier. Penny solves the mystery and has another scoop for the *Riverview Star*.

## 4. Behind the Green Door

1940 Edition. 211 Pages.

Somebody is tampering with a ski resort and a building next door has strange happenings behind a room with a green door. Penny gets the scoop on this to the *Star* via teletype before a rival reporter can signal her newspaper. Penny's reward is a new car for Christmas.

**3.**

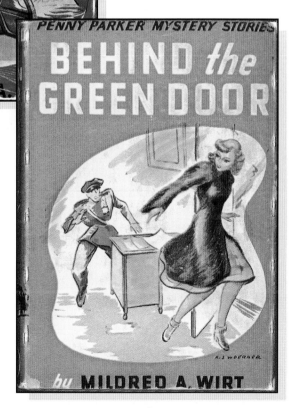

**4.**

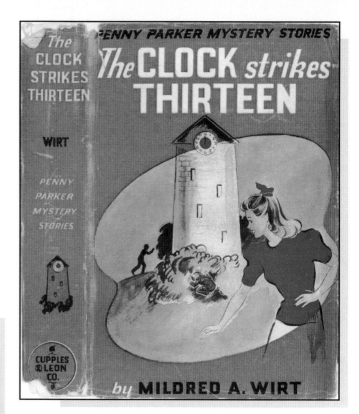

**5.**

**6.**

**8.**

## 5. Clue of the Silken Ladder

1941 Edition. 207 Pages.

Penny discovers a ladder made of silk in a curio shop operated by an unpleasant Japanese man. She discovers a connection between a gang of burglars and fake spiritualists and writes up her findings for the *Star*, for which she gets a raise in pay.

## 6. The Secret Pact

1941 Edition. 208 Pages.

Penny wants to write an article about a sailor's tattoo but both the *Star* and her high school newspaper reject the idea. She pursues her investigations and locates gold thieves. Penny's father promises to hire her new friend, Old Horney, as a pressman.

## 7. The Clock Strikes Thirteen

1942 Edition. 207 Pages.

Hooded night-riders are terrorizing farmers and Penny figures out the reason why.

## 8. The Wishing Well

1942 Edition. 206 Pages.

Penny explores the grounds of an old mansion and locates a wishing well that seems to have magical qualities.

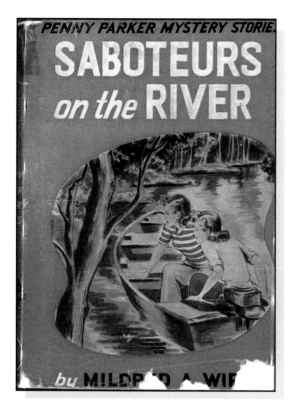

9.

10. *D.J. Layhe Collection.*

## 9. Saboteurs on the River

1943 Edition. 211 Pages.

Property is destroyed at a munitions factory. Penny seeks aid from a man named Old Noah who has an ark filled with animals. She rewards Old Noah for his idea of sending messages for help in corked bottles with a plan for him to live on a farm and travel around with his smaller animals in a truck.

## 10. Ghost Beyond the Gate

1943 Edition. 209 Pages.

Penny searches for her father who is kidnapped and solves mysteries associated with an old mansion.

## 11. Hoofbeats on the Turnpike

1944 Edition. 211 Pages.

Penny, who is broke, runs into an old man who shows her a newspaper clipping reading, "Five hundred dollars reward offered for any information leading to the capture of the Headless Horseman." Penny and her friend, Louise, search for Sleepy Hollow to collect this reward and travel to Red Valley where they are involved in a flood from a burst dam (12 years after Judy Bolton had the same experiences in *The Vanishing Shadow*). Penny finds the horseman, rescues a lady from the flood and has another scoop for the *Star*.

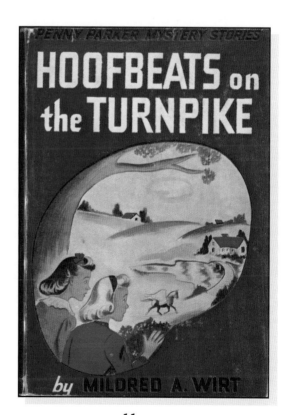

11.

12.

13.

14.

## 12. Voice From the Cave

1944 Edition. 204 Pages.

Penny, her father and his friend, Mrs. Deline, go to Sunset Beach for vacation. Penny solves mysteries concerning a shortwave radio station, a lighthouse, a thief, Mrs. Deline and a German submarine. This time Penny must keep her findings secret so as not to aid "the enemy."

## 13. Guilt of the Brass Thieves

1945 Edition. 210 Pages.

Mr. Gandiss and his seventeen-year-old son, Jack, enlist the help of Penny's father, publisher of the *Riverview Star*, to solve the problem of brass theft in their airplane factory. They become involved with another *River Queen*, this time a ferry that is later damaged, and watch Jack in a sailboat race. The race is won by Sally, Penny's newest best friend.

## 14. Signal in the Dark

1946 Edition. 210 Pages.

The *Star* hires Penny at a salary of $50 per week because of personnel shortages. Soon she is asked to cover an explosion at the Conway Steel Plant, which is possibly the work of saboteurs. (World War II stuff?)

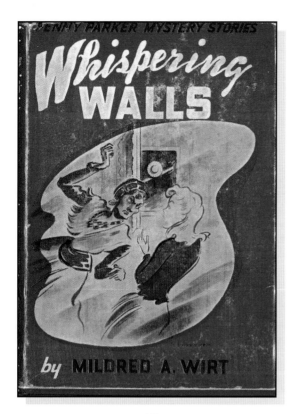

15.

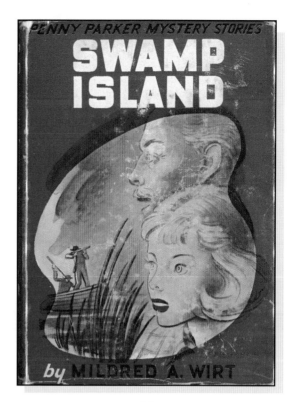

16.

## 15. Whispering Walls

1946 Edition. 212 Pages.

Mr. Rhett, a Riverview banker, and $250,000 in bank bonds is missing. Mrs. Rhett has come under the influence of servants who may have hidden agendas. Penny and her boyfriend, Jerry, figure all this out.

## 16. Swamp Island

1947 Edition. 203 Pages.

Penny encounters all sorts of people with problems and also dangerous wild boars while investigating happenings in a swamp. Mrs. Jones, one of the beneficiaries of Penny's investigations, sums it all up when she says, "The swamp always belongs to them that loves it."

## 17. The Cry at Midnight

1947 Edition. 207 Pages.

At midnight, Penny Parker and her best friends, Louise Sidell and Jerry Livingston, go skiing at Knob Hill, above town. They hear a cry coming from a nearby abandoned monastery. They learn it has been taken over by a weird religious cult. A precious gemstone that has been stolen also figures in the plot. Once all this is resolved, Penny says, "Just lead me to a typewriter!" This is the last line in a Penny Parker Mystery.

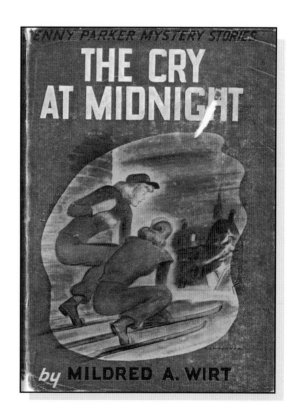

17.

# Bibliography

Billman, Carol. *The Secret of the Stratemeyer Syndicate.* The Ungar Publishing Company, New York, 1986.

Caprio, Betsy. *The Mystery of Nancy Drew: Girl Sleuth on the Couch.* Source Books, Trabuco Canyon, California, 1992.

Clarke, Laurie. *Clarke's Guide to Margaret Sutton's Judy Bolton Mystery Stories.* SynSine Press, Rheem Valley, California, 1995.

Farah, David. *Farah's Guide* (Tenth Printing). Farah's Books, Sunland, California, 1994.

Hoyt, Edwin P. *Horatio's Boys: The Life and Works of Horatio Alger, Jr.* Chilton Book Company, Radnor, Pennsylvania, 1974.

McFarlane, Leslie. *Ghost of the Hardy Boys.* Methuen/Two Continents, New York, 1976.

Nuschke, Marie Kathern. *The Dam That Could Not Break.* The Potter Enterprise, Coudersport, Pennsylvania, 1960.

Prager, Arthur. *Rascals at Large, or, The Clue in the Old Nostalgia.* Doubleday & Company, Inc., New York, 1971.

Society of Phantom Friends, The. *A Guide to Judy Bolton Country.* SynSine Press, Rheem Valley, California, 1997.

Society of Phantom Friends, The. *The Girls' Series Companion 1997 Edition.* SynSine Press, Rheem Valley, California, 1997.

# Periodicals

*Martha's KidLit Newsletter.* Martha Rasmussen, P.O. Box 1488, Ames, IA 50014. (Children's book lovers and collectors)

*Susabella Passengers and Friends.* Garrett Lothe, 80 Ocean Pines Lane, Pebble Beach, CA 93953. (Collectors and readers of all children's series books)

*The Whispered Watchword.* Kate Emburg, P.O. Box 1437, North Highlands, CA 95660. (Girls' series reading and collecting)

*Yellowback Library.* Gil O'Gara, P.O. Box 36172, Des Moines, IA 50315. (Juvenile series books, dime novels and related literature)

# About the Author

John Axe has written hundreds of research articles and many books about dolls, teddy bears and other collectibles. He is also an award-winning paper doll artist whose work has been used for Convention Souvenirs, journals and a series of paper doll books. He is the past editor of *Doll News,* the journal of the United Federation of Doll Clubs, Inc.

John designs teddy bears for Merrythought Limited, England's oldest toy company, and has won industry awards for this work.

For almost thirty years he has been a professor of Spanish and History and is still teaching History at Youngstown State University in Ohio.

John Axe has read and collected series books for more than fifty years. His collection includes every series book he ever had as a child and he has many hundreds of them. This life-long interest has now been recorded as *The Secret of Collecting Girls' Series Books, Featuring Nancy Drew®, Judy Bolton, Kay Tracey, Beverly Gray, Penny Parker and Ruth Fielding.* Of all series books, John likes best the Hardy Boys, the Albert Payson Terhune Dog Stories, the Five Little Peppers, the Heidi books and his favorite, the Judy Bolton Mystery Stories. Judy Bolton is the work of Margaret Sutton, whom he considers a great influence on his youth and the interests he developed in life.

*The Secret of Collecting Girls' Series Books, Featuring Nancy Drew®, Judy Bolton, Kay Tracey, Beverly Gray, Penny Parker and Ruth Fielding* is John Axe's 23rd book published by Hobby House Press, Inc.

## Author's Note

Even though I have read and handled almost every book mentioned in this work, it is possible that some inaccuracies have crept into it. I would appreciate any information and/or corrections that may be applied to any possible future editions. Correspondence may be addressed to the author in care of the publisher.